D1497777

ACA 115
STUDENT RESOURCE
WORKBOOK

Name: _____

Section: _____

Semester/Year: _____

Nash Community College • www.nashcc.edu

522 N. Old Carriage Road • Post Office Box 7488
Rocky Mount, North Carolina 27804-0488
Telephone: (252) 443-4011 • Fax: (252) 451-8401

Contents

ACA 115 ASSIGNMENTS AT A GLANCE

ASSIGNMENT	DUE DATE	SUBMITTED ☑	GRADE	NOTES
Scavenger Hunt				
Core 1: Course Management				
Core 2: Goal Setting				
Core 3: Study Skills				
Core 4: Tutorial/Library				
Core 5: Note Taking				
Core 6: Test Taking				
Journal – Entry 1-5				
Journal – Entry 6-10				
Final Project				

 Username & Password Information:

Program/Resource:	Username:	Password:
NCC Student E-mail	@st.nashcc.edu	
Moodle		
WebAdvisor		
CFNC.org		
Smart Thinking		

ASSIGNMENTS

- **Scavenger Hunt**
- **Core Assessment 1 Course Management System**
- **Core Assessment 2 Goal Setting**
- **Core Assessment 3 Study Skills**
- **Core Assessment 4 Tutorial and Learning Resources**
- **Core Assessment 5 Note Taking**
- **Core Assessment 6 Test Taking**
- **Final Project**

ACA Scavenger Hunt

Name: _____

Directions: Visit each location on campus and gather the requested information. If you do the scavenger hunt with a partner, each student should still complete and turn in separate copies with original signatures where requested.

Library:

What are the hours of operation? _____

List 2 magazine titles that are available in the library: _____

_____

List 2 DVD titles that are available in the library: _____

_____

Are the computers in the library available for students for any course work and internet research? _____

What is the current username and password used to access library resources from home? Username: _____ Password: _____

Signature of library employee: _____

Bookstore:

What are the hours of operation? _____

Name 5 things you can buy in the bookstore other than books. _____

_____

Advising:

What is your advisor's name and office number? _____

List your advisor's office hours: _____

Obtain a copy of your degree checklist. Degree checklists can often be found outside of the department chair's door and/or online on the College's website.

Website:

Home | Contact Us | WebAdvisor
Employee Email | Student Email | Moodle
Faculty/Staff Resources

Go to the college website home page and locate the portal of links shown to the right. (It's located in the upper right hand corner.) Click on **Student Email**. What do you do if you need login help with your *student email*? _____

Click on the **Moodle** link. Find the instructions on how to recover your Moodle password. What is the first step? _____

Username [|]

Password [   ] Login

☐ Remember username

Forgotten your username or password?

Prospective Students

Students

Finally, click on the **WebAdvisor** link. Select the Students menu. Find and select the link with the question "What's my password?" From the options listed, which statement would you click on if you forgot your password?

_____

COMMUNITY From the college website's home page, locate and hold the cursor over the word "Community." Choose the "EmploymeNCC" link. Click the "Students Find Jobs!" blue button.

List one of the two NCC contact names listed: _____

Register if you are interested by selecting "Click Here to Register."

From the college website's home page, locate and hold the cursor over the "About NCC" (Located at the bottom left hand corner of the changing banner photo.) Choose the "Bookstore" link from the list. This takes you to the online bookstore. In the "Books" drop down menu in the upper left, select "Textbooks & Course Materials." Find for the current textbook to COM 231. Select the current term; the department is COM; the course number is 231, pick any section; click SUBMIT.

List the title of the book: _____

How much is the book if purchased new? _____ Used? _____

Current Students From the College's website, click on the "Current Students" tab.

What is the e-mail address for the Financial Aid office?

_____

Next, locate the orange "Students" tab on the bottom right hand side of the screen. Select the "Campus Tutoring" option. Locate the PAL Tutor Connection Program. Student's interested in tutoring need to complete what?

_____

Math Assessment Center:
(Locate the testing center on the first floor of the S&T building.)

What does a student need in order to make up a test? _____

What are the hours that the testing center is available for make-up testing?

_____

What personal item should be left in your book bag or at the front desk?

_____

Signature of center employee: _____

Student and Enrollment Services (SES):
If you do not already have a student ID, get your ID made at Student and Enrollment Services.

List at least one service that SES provides: _____

_____

Signature of SES employee: _____

Miscellaneous:
Where is the campus radio station located? _____

What is the name of the building where the cashier's office is located? _____

Where do you go to eat on campus? _____

Where is lost and found located? _____

Where is Cosmetology located? _____

What is the minimum GPA required to maintain financial aid? _____

Core Assessment 1   Due Date: _____

Course Management System Learning Outcome:
Students will access and utilize a campus course management system.

In-Class Assignment: Locate the WebAdvisor, Student Email and Moodle links from the Nash Community College website, successfully log in and complete the following tasks.

Complete the following tasks in **WebAdvisor**:

WebAdvisor

☐ 1. Access WebAdvisor and log in. (See page 11 in workbook for access and log in information.) If it is your first time logging in you will be asked to change your password. Be sure to select something you can remember. (Consider using the same password for all your campus accounts.) If you need your WebAdvisor password reset, you can do so directly from WebAdvisor before logging in. Select the "Student" menu, click on the link, "What's my password?" and follow the instructions.

☐ 2. After successfully logging into WebAdvisor, select the "STUDENTS MENU," then select "My Profile."

☐ 3. What is the name of your advisor? _____

☐ 4. What is your 7 digit student ID? _____

☐ 5. Here, when viewing the "My Profile" screen, you will see the most current personal information that NCC has for you on record.
Verify your address and phone number. Complete the "Contact Information Verification Form" found on page 9 in this workbook. Turn in the form to your instructor.

   If your contact information was incorrect when you selected "My Profile," select OK at the bottom of the screen. This will take you back to the "Students Menu." Select "Student Forms." Select, "Change of Contact Information." Complete the Change of Contact Information Form and select, "Submit."

☐ 4. Obtain a printout of your Program Evaluation. From the student menu, click on "Program Evaluation" located on the right hand side of the screen under "Academic Profile." Print. **Do not turn this into your instructor! Keep this in a safe place, you will need this for the Core Assessment 2: Goal Setting project.**

STUDENT EMAIL

Complete the following tasks in **Student Email**:

☐ 1. Access Student Email and log in. (See page 12 in this workbook for access and log in information.)

☐ 2. Using quality e-mail etiquette (see page 13 in this workbook), send your ACA instructor an e-mail introducing yourself <u>and</u> describing your favorite thing about Nash Community College.

To Lisa Cooper ×   Cc

Introduction & ACA Assignment

☐ 3. Using quality e-mail etiquette, compose an e-mail of introduction to your advisor and in the "CC" line, include your ACA instructor. You can locate your advisor's e-mail address by typing their name in the "To" line. In the "Subject" line, type "Introduction and ACA assignment." <u>Be sure to introduce yourself, let them know they are your advisor and that you look forward to working with them.</u>

Complete the following tasks in **Moodle:**

☐ 1. Access Moodle and log in. (See page 14 in this workbook for access and log in information.) Select this specific course from the list, "ACA Success and Study Skills."

ḿoodle

☐ 2. To review specific information about this course, Access the course "Syllabus" from the General Welcome block.

☐ 3. Select the "   Scavenger Hunt Quiz" under assignments from the Session 2 block and t☑: the quiz.

☐ 4. Enter the " On Campus Helpful Advice Forum" under assignments from the Session 2 block. Post a reply and feel free to respond to other student posts. Note that this is a single simple discussion forum. Just to make you aware, there are different types of forum formats instructors can use, such as allowing you to start a new discussion topic.

☐ 5. If you haven't already done so, add a picture to your profile. Follow the instructions on page 15 of this workbook. There is also a how-to video located in the Moodle Session 2 block. (Your instructor MAY award extra credit to students who add a profile picture!)

☐ 6. Access grades. From the Settings block under "Course Administration," select Grades. Make sure "user report" is selected. This gives you detailed information on the specific course. Print a copy and submit to your ACA instructor. Note, the "overview report" shows you an overview of all the courses you are enrolled in.

Settings
▼ Course administration
  Turn editing on
  Edit settings
  Completion tracking
  ▶ Users
  Grades

☐ 7. After completing every item for this entire Core Assessment 1, open the " Core Assessment 1 Reflection Questionnaire" under assignments from the Session 2 block. Complete and submit.

Documentation of Completion

The instructor will have:
1. the completed "Contact Information Verification Form"
2. the e-mail "introduction" sent from the student
3. the e-mail sent to the student's advisor (cc instructor)
4. printout of grades from Moodle
5. submission of completed Reflection Form Questionnaire via Moodle
6. completion of Scavenger Hunt quiz in Moodle
7. participation in a Forum in Moodle

Contact Information Verification Form

Complete and submit this form to your ACA instructor.

Name: _____

Record the phone number **displayed** in WebAdvisor from the student menu under "My Profile."

_____

Is that information correct? Yes _____   No _____

If NO, please:
1. Record the correct phone number to best reach you: _____
                                -and-
Select "Student Forms." Under the STUDENTS MENU. Select, "Change of Contact Information." Complete the Change of Contact Information Form and select, "Submit."

  Note: ALL changes of address, phone or major need to be submitted to Student and Enrollment Services on a timely basis. Change of Contact Information forms are located in WebAdvisor at all times.

****

I attest that I have verified my contact information and made any necessary corrections by completing a Change of Information Form and submitting it to Student and Enrollment Services.

_____

Signature

ACA Course Management System
CORE ASSESSMENT 1 EVALUATION RUBRIC

STUDENT NAME_____

Student submits Contact Information Verification Form	10	
Student sends introduction e-mail to instructor.	10	
Introduction e-mail is well-developed including required information, and elaboration.	0-10	
Student sends e-mail to advisor.	10	
Student demonstrates quality e-mail etiquette.	0-10	
Student completes Scavenger Hunt Quiz in Moodle.	10	
Student responds to a discussion forum prompt in Moodle.	10	
Student's discussion forum response demonstrates care and thought and/or student posts multiple times.	0-10	
Student submits print out of grades from Moodle.	10	
Student completes CA1 Reflection Questionnaire in Moodle.	10	
TOTAL POINTS	(0-100)	
LETTER GRADE		
RUBRIC SCORE	(0-4)	

GRADE RANGE	RUBRIC SCORE	DESCRIPTION
90-100	4	Exceeds Expectations
80-89	3	Meets Expectations
60-79	2	Partially Meets Expectations
1-59	1	Did Not Meet Expectations
0	0	Did Not Attempt Assignment

<u>WebAdvisor Basics</u>

WebAdvisor is the portal that Nash Community College uses to allow students to register for classes, review financial aid information, and review grades online. WebAdvisor processes registration requests based on class availability and is able to determine if course prerequisites have been met. WebAdvisor is accessed with a secure username and password. This helps the college keep student information confidential and secure.

Where can I find WebAdvisor?

How do I Log In to WebAdvisor?

1. All student accounts (current and new) must be activated prior to logging into WebAdvisor. New student activation will begin the first day of class.

2. Go to www.nashcc.edu. Follow the directions above by clicking on the "Student Portal" button on the Nash CC homepage. Click on WebAdvisor, and then click "Log In".

3. Your **username** is your first initial, middle initial, last name and the last 3 digits of your student ID (all lowercase, no spaces, no punctuation).
   Example: Name: John Allen Smith   Student ID: 2563244   Username: jasmith244.

4. Your **password** is Ncc plus your date of birth using 2 digits each for month, day, and year (no spaces, no punctuation). Example: John's Birthday: February 6, 1981, Password: Ncc020681. You will be able to change this password after your first successful login.

5. Once you click "Submit" it will say that your "password has expired". Re-enter your username and password and enter in a new password **(Your password needs to be between 6 and 9 characters and must have both letters and numbers)**.

6. Click "Students" to access your information.

*If you are unable to log in or have forgotten your password, click on "Students" and "What is my User ID?" or "What is my password?" For verification purposes, they will be sent to your Student Email.

Nash CC Student Email

Gmail (Student Email) is Nash Community College's official means of communication to students. You will receive important information about your Financial Aid, updates from your instructors, and any other valuable information that you will be responsible for knowing while you are at Nash CC through Student Email.

Get in the habit of checking your Nash CC Student Email on a daily basis!

How to Log-in to Student Email:

1. Go to www.nashcc.edu. Follow the directions above by clicking on the "Student Portal" button on the Nash CC homepage.
2. Next, click on the "Student Email" button. This will take you straight to the Student Email log in screen.
3. Your **username** is your first initial, middle initial, last name and the last 3 digits of your student ID   (all lowercase, no spaces, no punctuation).
   Example: Name: John Allen Smith   Student ID: 2563244   Username: jasmith244.
4. Your **password** is Ncc plus your date of birth using 2 digits each for month, day, and year (no spaces, no punctuation). Example: John's birthday is February 6, 1981—Password: Ncc020681. You will be able to change this password after you first successful login.
5. Once you have entered your login information, click 'Sign In'
6. After you have read the Terms of Service, click "I accept". Continue to my account.
7. You will be asked to set a new password.
8. Enter your initial password, then enter your new password twice. Try to choose a strong password. The password strength can be determined by looking at the bar on the right of the password fields.
9. Click the 'Submit' button. You will be taken to your new inbox.

* For log in assistance, in the Student Portal, click on "Log In Help" under Student Email. At the top of the page, you can submit a help ticket for forgotten passwords.

Basic College E-mail Etiquette

Subject line: Always use a meaningful subject to help the recipient know the content of the message. Failure to do so with an instructor might result in the message being discarded as spam.

Greeting: Just like a written letter, open your e-mail with a greeting like Dear Dr. West or Dear Mrs. Cooper.

Identify yourself: Your instructors (or advisor) may have over one hundred students in any given semester. Put your name and the course at the beginning of the e-mail to help identify who you are and the subject for which you are requesting information.

Grammar: Always use correct spelling, grammar, and punctuation in an e-mail. Do not use text messaging abbreviations. Avoid typing an e-mail in all capital letters, which is often perceived as yelling. Spell check and proofread the message before you send it.

Length: Use short paragraphs, be concise, and get to the point. Do not make the e-mail longer than it needs to be for your question or concern.

Purpose: Make sure that e-mail is an appropriate venue for your concern. If you really need to meet face-to-face with your instructor, send an e-mail to set up an appointment, but save the rest of the conversation for when you meet with them. Don't try to use e-mail to replace a face-to-face conversation if the face-to-face meeting is what is really needed.

Courtesy: "Speak" to people electronically in the same manner you would speak to them face-to-face. Re-read the e-mail to ensure that the tone is what you intended.

Closing: Always end a message with your name and basic contact information, particularly if your peers or instructor need to respond to you. Consider including your first and last name, phone number, and e-mail address

References

Email Etiquette: http://owl/english/purdue.edu/owl/resource/636/01.
Fundamentals of College Email Etiquette:
http://school.tips.net/Pages/T007953 Fundamentals of College Email Etiquette.html
SCC Email Etiquette and Appropriate Use of Distribution Lists:
http://www.scc.losrios.edu/FacultyStaffPublications and Marketing Guide/E-mail/SCC Email Etiquette and Appropriate Use of Distribution Lists.htm
eMail Etiquette: http://www.dawsoncollege.qc.ca/info-desk/web-tutorials/email-etiquette

MOODLE Basics

What is Moodle?

Moodle is an online course management system that can be used for all classes, including online, hybrid, virtual, and on campus- classroom based courses. Instructors will post course syllabi, grades, assignments, and documents in Moodle.

Where can I find Moodle?

How do I Log In to Moodle?

1. As a student, you will be able to access your Moodle course(s) on the first day of class each semester. (If you are taking an online course, you will be required to log into Moodle and complete an Enrollment Verification Activity—the due date for this assignment will be posted in Moodle. Students who do not complete this assignment by the due date will be dropped from the online course—this does not include hybrid courses).

2. Go to www.nashcc.edu. Follow the directions above by clicking on the "Student Portal" button on the Nash CC homepage. Click Moodle and under "Log In" you will type in your username and password.

3. Your username is your first initial, middle initial, last name and the last 3 digits of your student ID (all lowercase, no spaces, no punctuation). Example: Name: John Allen Smith Student ID: 2563244 Username: jasmith244.

4. Your password is Ncc plus your date of birth using 2 digits each for month, day, and year (no spaces, no punctuation). Example: John's Birthday: February 6, 1981, Password: Ncc020681. You will be able to change this password after your first successful login.

5. Once you click "Login" you will be prompted to change your password. For security purposes, please do not share this password with anyone.

*If you fail to log in successfully go to the Online Support Center—located on the Moodle home page.

Moodle Basics: How to Upload a Picture to Moodle (iPad Views)

To upload a picture select your name to edit your profile.

Select Edit profile.

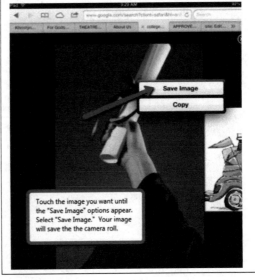

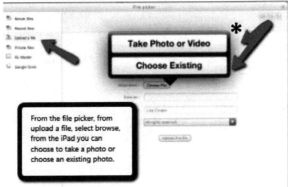

Take Photo or Video

Choose Existing

*

From the file picker, from upload a file, select browse, from the iPad you can choose to take a photo or choose an existing photo.

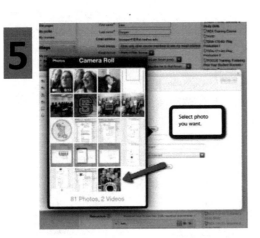

* NOTE – You can take a photo of yourself in class with the iPad camera and it will appear on the camera roll for you to upload. OR you can select any picture or icon from the internet and save it to the camera roll on the iPad and upload it to Moodle as described.

Save Image

Copy

Touch the image you want until the "Save Image" options appear. Select "Save Image." Your image will save the the camera roll.

5

Camera Roll

Select photo you want.

81 Photos, 2 Videos

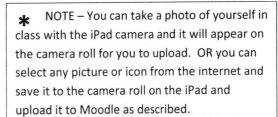

6

Select Update profile.

Core Assessment 2   Due Date: _____

Goal Setting Learning Outcome:

Students will set personal and academic goals, explore career options, and develop a semester-by-semester plan of study through degree completion.

1. SMARTEST Goals Worksheets

Complete the SMARTEST Goals Worksheet for your academic/ professional life and personal life found on pages 20-22 in this workbook. Submit completed worksheets to the instructor at the end of the class period.

2. Career Assessment (Complete in–class as time and technology permit)

☐ Complete the **"Interest Profiler"** under the *Learn About Yourself* menu from the "Plan for a Career" tab at CFNC.org

a. In Moodle, from the Session block under assignments access the link " 📄 Interest Profiler from CFNC. Org." For your reference here is the direct link to the CFNC Interest Profiler: https://www1.cfnc.org/Plan/For_A_Career/Learn_About_Yourself/Learn_About_Yourself.aspx

b. Select the Interest Profiler button. You will be prompted to set up an account first to complete the "Interest Profiler." After setting up your account, you should be re-directed back to the "Interest Profiler."

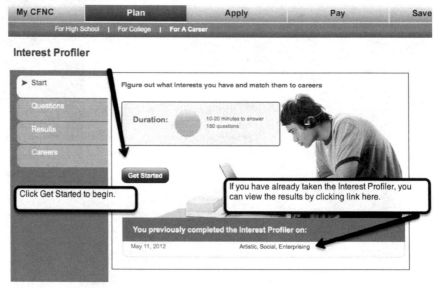

☐ Type a minimum 5 sentence reflection regarding your results in the space provide at the bottom of your results page.

☐ Print out the results, review and submit a copy to your instructor.

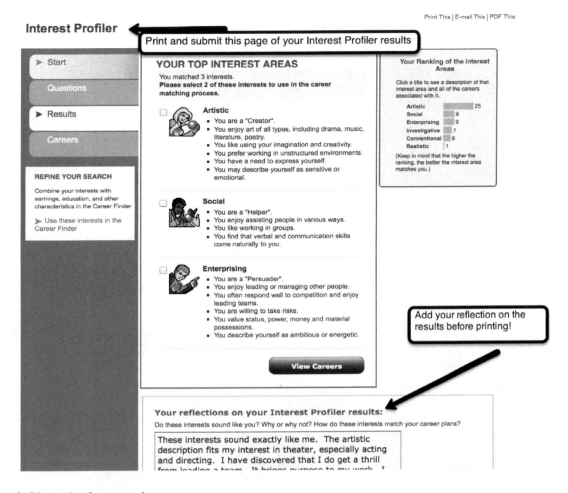

Out-of-Class Assignment

3. Semester-by-Semester Plan of Study

☐ **Make an appointment** with your advisor before the registration period to create a plan of study.

☐ **Bring** the 4 following items to the meeting with your advisor:

a) Degree checklist - Degree checklists can often be found outside of the department chair's door and/or online on the College's website.

b) Program Evaluation - **You should have printed this while completing Core Assessment 1.** The Program Evaluation can be found on WebAdvisor. To do so, click on "Students." "Program Evaluation" is on the right hand side of the screen under "Academic Profile."

c) Advisor Questionnaire – A hard copy is located on a page 24 in the workbook. An electronic copy can be found in Moodle under assignments in the Session block, titled " Advisor Questionnaire."

d) Semester-by-Semester Plan of Study Form: Brainstorm ideas for future semesters' coursework, and consider any transfer plans, if applicable, before the meeting. A hard copy of the form is located in your workbook on page 23. An electronic copy can be found in Moodle under assignments in the Session block titled " Semester-by-Semester Plan of Study Form."

☐ **At the meeting, work jointly** with your advisor to develop your **Semester-by-Semester Plan of Study** through graduation.
   a) Take from the meeting a hardcopy of the completed Semester-by-Semester Plan of Study.
   b) Ask if your advisor can e-mail you a copy of the Semester-by-Semester Plan of Study so that each has an electronic file for future reference and modification.
   c) Ask your advisor to complete the Advisor Questionnaire and give it back to you for submission.

Advisor Responsibilities:

1. The advisor and student should jointly develop a plan of study for the student through degree completion. Each individual should leave the meeting with a copy of the Semester-by-Semester Plan of Study.
2. Ideally, the advisor should e-mail the student a copy of the Semester-by-Semester Plan of Study so that each has an electronic file for future reference and modification.
3. The advisor will complete the Advisor Questionnaire and return it to the student at the meeting.

Helpful Hints:

1. Make an appointment with your advisor in advance. **Keep the appointment!** If an emergency arises, contact the advisor to reschedule.
2. Come prepared with all of the documents mentioned above: Degree Checklist, Program Evaluation, Plan of Study, and Advisor Questionnaire.

Documentation needed for completion of assignment:

1. SMARTEST Goals Worksheets
2. copy of "Interest Profiler" results from CFNC.org
3. completed Semester-By-Semester Plan of Study
4. completed Advisor Questionnaire

ACA Goal Setting
CORE ASSESSMENT 2 EVALUATION RUBRIC

STUDENT NAME_____

Student Completes all portions of the SMARTEST Goals Worksheets with thought & care	0-30	
Student completes "Interest Profiler" Career Assessment	15	
Student's "Interest Profiler" includes a thoughtful reflection.	0-10	
Student completes signed Plan of Study Form.		
• Completes form for one semester	15	
• Completes form through degree completion	15	
Student meets with advisor to develop plan of study.	15	
TOTAL POINTS	(0-100)	
LETTER GRADE		
RUBRIC SCORE	(0-4)	

CORE EVALUATION RUBRIC

GRADE RANGE	RUBRIC SCORE	DESCRIPTION
90-100	4	Exceeds Expectations
80-89	3	Meets Expectations
60-79	2	Partially Meets Expectations
1-59	1	Did Not Meet Expectations
0	0	Did Not Attempt Assignment

SMARTEST Goals Worksheet: Core Assessment 2

NAME: _____ DATE_____

My Academic/Professional Goal: _____
_____

My Personal Goal: _____
_____

Complete this worksheet to make sure your goals are the SMARTEST!

S- Specific	*What exactly do you want to accomplish? Be as specific as possible. For example, a general goal would be, "Get in shape" but a specific goal would say, "Get in shape by joining a health club and working out 3 days a week."* <u>**Academic/Professional Goal:**</u> <u>**Personal Goal:**</u>
M-Measurable	*How will you know when you have reached this goal? Be concrete.* <u>**Academic/Professional Goal:**</u> <u>**Personal Goal:**</u>
A-Achievable	*Is achieving this goal realistic with effort and commitment? Have you got the resources to achieve this goal? If not, how will you get them? Who are the people you can go to for help?* <u>**Academic/Professional Goal:**</u> <u>**Personal Goal:**</u>

R- Relevant	*Why is this goal important to your life? What are the benefits to achieving this goal?*
	Academic/Professional Goal:
	Personal Goal:
T-Time-bound	*When will you achieve this goal? With no time frame tied to it there's no sense of urgency. "Someday" won't work. But if you anchor it within a timeframe, "by May 1, 2016", then you've set your mind into motion to begin.*
	Academic/Professional Goal:
	Personal Goal:
E-Exhibit	*How will you display your goals so that you are reminded of them every day?*
	Academic/Professional Goal:
	Personal Goal:

S-Specific Action Step	*What smaller steps need to be taken to get you to your goal?* **Academic/Professional Goal:**

Action Step	Expected Completion Date
O	
O	
O	
O	
O	

Personal Goal:

Action Step	Expected Completion Date
O	
O	
O	
O	
O	

T- Target Obstacles	*What are some obstacles you might face and what steps can you take to meet these challenges?* **Academic/Professional Goal:**

Potential Obstacles	Potential Solutions

Personal Goal:

Potential Obstacles	Potential Solutions

Semester-by-Semester Plan of Study

Student Name:	ID #
Major:	Code:
Advisor:	Phone #

Semester	
Total	

Semester	
Total	

Semester	
Total	

Semester	
Total	

Semester	
Total	

Semester	
Total	

Semester	
Total	

Semester	
Total	

Semester	
Total	

Total Credit Hours:

Advisor Signature: Student Signature:

Date: Click here to enter a date.

Advisor Questionnaire

Advisor:

Student:

ACA Instructor:

Date of Meeting:

Did the student bring any of the following to the meeting?

Departmental Degree Check sheet	☐ YES	☐ NO
Printout of Program Evaluation	☐ YES	☐ NO
Semester-By-Semester Plan of Study	☐ YES	☐ NO
with some ideas filled-in	☐ YES	☐ NO

ADVISOR, COMPLETE AND RETURN TO STUDENT AT THE MEETING

_____

Advisor Signature

Core Assessment 3   **Due Date:** _____

Study Skills Learning Outcome:
Students will define and explain strategies for effective studying.

Name: _____

In Class Assignment: Complete the following tasks in order to gain a true understanding of the type of learner you are, how you learn best, and ways you can improve your academic performance.

1. **VARK Learning Style Assessment:** Complete the assessment in order to identify your primary VARK learning style.

   a. In Moodle, find and click on the "VARK Learning Style Assessment" under Session 4.
   b. This will open a new window, read the directions and take the assessment. It is only 16 questions, answer them honestly. Then click, OK.
   c. A new window with your results will show, print this page.
   d. You will submit the results page to your instructor on the due date.
   e. Determine your VARK Learning Style by looking at the numbers on your results page. Circle the learning style with the largest number.
   f. Which learning style did you circle? _____
   g. You have now identified your VARK Learning Style!

2. **Learning Style Research:** Conduct research on your primary learning style.

   a. Complete the graphical organizer on pages 27 & 28 in an effort to obtain a deeper understanding and identify strategies and characteristics.
   b. You will use this research as a base to create your Learning Style Project (see Out of Class Assignment).

Out of Class Assignment: Complete the following tasks in order to apply the knowledge you gained during your Learning Style Research.

3. **Learning Style Project:** Complete only one of the projects from the options listed for your learning style. (For example, if you are a visual learner, you may only choose from 1-V Flow Chart or 2-V Mind Map.) The project options begin on page 29.
   Your Learning Style Research should be reflected in this project.

ACA Study Skills
CORE ASSESSMENT 3 EVALUATION RUBRIC

Student Name: _____

Learning Style Evaluated: ☐ Visual ☐ Aural ☐ Read/Write ☐ Kinesthetic

Specific Assignment Completed: _____

VARK Learning Style Assessment		
Student completes and submits the VARK Learning Styles Assessment.	15	
Learning Style Research		
Student submits completed Learning Style Research	5	
Student appropriately defines his/her preferred learning style and identifies the appropriate characteristics.	0-10	
Student appropriately identifies strengths and weaknesses of his/her preferred learning style.	0-10	
Student appropriately identifies study tips for his/her preferred learning style.	0-10	
Student completes reflection on preferred learning style and using learned information, the student develops a plan for success in an additional course in which they are enrolled.	0-10	
Learning Style Project		
Student completes one of the project options from their preferred learning style.	10	
Student follows the assignment-specific instructions. (It is typed if required; includes citation of sources if required; includes any required documentation or visual aid, etc.)	0-10	
Student's assignment is well executed, accurate, neat, and organized. It demonstrates planning, effort and attention to detail.	0-10	
Student's assignment demonstrates a higher level of thought and depth of understanding for the study process and learning style.	0-10	
TOTAL POINTS	(0-100)	
LETTER GRADE		
RUBRIC SCORE	(0-4)	

GRADE RANGE	RUBRIC SCORE	DESCRIPTION
90-100	4	Exceeds Expectations
80-89	3	Meets Expectations
60-79	2	Partially Meets Expectations
1-59	1	Did Not Meet Expectations

0	0	Did Not Attempt Assignment

Learning Style Research

Directions: Using your primary learning style, complete the following graphical organizer in an effort to obtain a deeper understanding and identify strategies and characteristics.

What type of learner are you?

Definition:
(Define/Explain your learning style.)

Strengths:
(Identify 3 strengths that are typical for your learning style.)

1.

2.

3.

Characteristics of my learning style:
(Identify 5 characteristics of your learning style.)

1.

2.

3.

4.

5.

Weaknesses:
(Identify 3 weaknesses that are typical for your learning style.)

1.

2.

3.

28

Study Tips...
for my learning style:
(Identify 10 study tips for your learning style.)

1.

2.

3.

4.

5.

6.

7.

8.

9.

10.

Learning Style Reflection:
(Were you classified as the type of learner that you thought you were? After doing research, do you agree or disagree with your results?)

_____

_____

_____

_____

_____

_____

Applying Your Knowledge

Identify a course (other than ACA) you are currently taking:

_____

How will you use the knowledge you've gained to ensure success in the course listed above?

_____

_____

_____

_____

_____

_____

_____

_____

_____

_____

_____

Learning Style Project Options

Only complete ONE project from your learning style!

Visual Learning Style Options

Select one of the following options if "Visual" is your primary learning style.

1. **Flow chart-** Make a flowchart to show how you will use visual learning strategies to proceed *before, during,* and *after* a test. The flowchart should demonstrate a step-by-step process students should go through to effectively study. Personalize the chart to show exactly what you do or should do as a visual learner. Be as clear and specific as possible when sharing the strategies. Plan to present your flowchart to the class. The flowchart can be handmade or computer-generated.

    ### A Quality Flowchart:
    - *Is neat, clear and demonstrates thought and planning*
    - *Is visually attractive and readily understood*
    - *Contains the 3 categories: Before, During and After*
    - *Contains a minimum of 10 steps*

2. **Mind Map/Poster -** Create a mind map self-portrait or a poster of you and how you learn. (See sample created on FreeMind on workbook page 35.) With you in the center of your mind map, be sure to include at least 6 branches (such as ideal study conditions; interests; preferred teaching styles; preferred learning styles; memorization; study tips; etc.) and all the necessary supporting sub-branches (minimum of 3 per branch.) Your mind map can be hand drawn or you can download several free mind map software programs if you want to create a computer generated mind map. Care should be evident in its creation. Present your mind map to your classmates.

    ### A Quality Mind Map/Poster:
    - *Is neat, clear and demonstrates thought and planning*
    - *Contains at least 6 main branches with a minimum of 3 supporting sub-branches per main branch*
    - *Uses a minimum of 6 different colors*
    - *Contains a minimum of 6 icons or pictures*
    - *Follows the guidelines for good mind map structure*

Aural Learning Style Assignment Options

Select one of the following options if "Aural" is your primary learning style.

1. ***Radio Talk Show-*** Create and record a radio show or podcast about how aural learners learn, how they should study, and share a few tips for an ideal study environment. Your show could be a call-in show with questions you answer or a public service announcement / infomercial. Make sure to include at least two main ideas from each of the topics: how aural learners learn, how they should study, and tips for an ideal study environment. The length of the final product (show or infomercial) should be between 3-5 minutes. Bring a printed transcript for your instructor and an audio copy to play in class. <u>Special note:</u> Consider using the college's radio station to help with your project or possibly broadcast it when complete! The radio station is located in the Business & Industry building, phone, 451-8486 or email at <u>nashradio@st.nashcc.edu</u>.

   ### *A Quality Radio Show:*
   - *Demonstrates research and understanding of the aural learning style*
   - *Includes at least two main ideas from the three topics provided*
   - *Is between 3-5 minutes in length*
   - *Demonstrates care and planning*

(2-A) ***Storytelling-*** Develop and type a script for a movie or play comparing an aural learner's poor study habits and their pitfalls to recommended/good study habits for aural learners and their benefits. The storyline should be thoughtful and coherent exemplifying an understanding of aural learners as well as show care and planning. Turn the story into a video clip/animation using an electronic resource such as goanimate.com. See "RESOURCES" at the end of the Core 3 Learning Style Project Options." Bring a printed copy of your script for your instructor and be prepared to share your video with the class.

A Quality Storytelling Product:
- *Is at least 2 pages typed and is in proper script/dialogue format*
- *Tells a clear story from start to finish about good versus bad study habits*
- *Reflects an understanding of aural learners based on what the characters say and do*
- *Has been proofread/edited for grammatical and mechanical issues*

Read/Write Learning Style Assignment Options

Select one of the following options if "Read/Write" is your primary learning style.

(1-R) Case Study- Read a case study and then <u>type</u> a minimum 2-page report on your selected case study answering the questions under the case study's character's name.

Select **ONLY ONE** of the three student case stories:

- *Tammy Ko (Chapter 3)*
    1. What do you have in common with Tammy? How are you managing the situation so you can be successful?
    2. Is Tammy smart? If so, in what ways? What is she particularly good at? What multiple intelligences seem to be her strong suit?
    3. What sensory modality does Tammy prefer for taking in information? Does she learn best by viewing information through charts and graphs, by talking and listening, by reading and writing or by actually doing things? How are you able to draw that conclusion?
    4. What are the differences between Mr. Caldwell's teaching style and Tammy's learning style? How do these differences affect Tammy's learning?
    5. What should Tammy do to become a better learner in Mr. Caldwell's class?
    6. Consider the possible outcomes for Tammy and finish your paper with a paragraph or two ending Tammy's story and the case study.
- *Kevin Baxter (Chapter 9)*
    1. What do you have in common with Kevin? How are you managing the situation so you can be successful?
    2. Why is Kevin experiencing problems remembering course content in his philosophy class? List 5 reasons you identify from the case study.
    3. Is Kevin too old to learn? Why or why not?
    4. Identify, discuss and exemplify five memory techniques that Kevin could use to help him memorize all the names and terms he needs to know.
    5. Consider the possible outcomes for Kevin and finish your paper with a paragraph or two ending Kevin's story and the case study.
- *Katie Alexander (Chapter 8)*
    1. What do you have in common with Katie? How are you managing the situation so you can be successful?
    2. Katie is probably an intelligent student, but she has decided that she dislikes reading and studying, so she avoids it. Elaborate on

how important these two skills will be as she continues to pursue a college degree? Is she likely to succeed her second time around? Why or why not?

3. How would you characterize Katie as a student? Identify five specific problems described in the case study that could interfere with her college success.
4. Identify three specific things Katie should do to get her college career on track.
5. Consider the possible outcomes for Katie and finish your paper with a paragraph or two ending Katie's story and the case study.

A Quality Case Study:

- *Is at least 2 full pages (typed and double-spaced) in length*
- *Shows evidence of having read the text in the form of examples and/or direct quotes*
- *Fully answers all questions posed*
- *Has been proofread for grammatical and mechanical issues*

(2-R) Resource Handout- Using the information you gained while completing your Learning Style Research as well as additional research, create a handout for your classmates that has tips for read/write learners as well as useful websites for help with studying. Summarize your findings in a typed hand out that you will share with all of your classmates. Make sure to include suggestions for read/write learners and describe each website in detail <u>using your own words</u>. Include examples of the useful information found at the site. Include all references for easy access.

A Quality Resource Handout:

- *Includes at least 5 suggestions for read/write learners*
- *Summarizes/assesses at least 5 websites to assist read/write learners*
- *Is at least 2 full pages (typed and double-spaced) in length*
- *Is neat, attractive, and contains all information a student would need to find the website*
- *Has been proofread for grammatical and mechanical issues*

Kinesthetic Learning Style Assignment Options

Select one of the following options if "Kinesthetic" is your primary learning style.

(1-K) **Scrapbook-** Create a colorful, dynamic scrapbook that shows a portrait of a kinesthetic learner. The scrapbook should include pages on how a kinesthetic learner learns, how they should adapt in a classroom that does not lend itself to their learning style, poor study habits for kinesthetic learners, good study habits for kinesthetic learners, and a plan to implement at least 3 new techniques that you have discovered during your research.

A Quality Scrapbook:
- *Is attractive, neat and organized showing evidence of care and planning*
- *Includes pictures, photographs or drawings*
- *Includes pages on how a kinesthetic learner learns, how they should adapt in a classroom that does not lend itself to their learning style, poor study habits for kinesthetic learners, good study habits for kinesthetic learners, and a plan to implement at least 3 new techniques that you have discovered during your research.*

(2-K) **Webpage-** Create a Web Page that displays a portrait of how a kinesthetic learner learns, how they should adapt in a classroom that does not lend itself to their learning style, poor study habits for kinesthetic learners, good study habits for kinesthetic learners, and a plan to implement at least 3 new techniques that you have discovered during your research. There should be at least five details/examples for each topic. You should include at least one link per topic (a minimum of five links). The webpage should be visually appealing, easy to navigate, organized, and accurate with properly cited content. You will show the webpage to the class as well as provide access information to your instructor. Note, you are expected to create a webpage prototype but actually publishing it to the web is optional.

A Quality Webpage:
- *Is attractive, easy to navigate and organized*
- *Shows evidence of care and planning*
- *Includes a minimum of five details/examples for each topic.*
- *Includes a minimum of one link per topic (a minimum of five links).*

RESOURCES FOR ALL ASSIGNMENT OPTIONS:

Direct links can be found on Moodle under assignments in the Session 4 block in a resource titled " Links to core 3 study skills resources for all assignments."

1. glogster.com : A Glog is an interactive visual platform in which users create a "poster or web page" containing multimedia elements including: text, audio, video, images, graphics, drawings, and data. http://www.glogster.com/

2. Comic Creator: If you just search comic creator, you may find several websites to help you develop a storyboard, comic strip etc. Once such link is http://www.readwritethink.org/files/resources/interactives/comic/index.html

3. Xtranormal: With Xtranormal, you can create animated movies. You simply select certain settings, type dialogue and action and cool stuff happens. For example, there is a "superheroes" Geico commercial running that was created using Xtranormal. You will need to create an account, and there is a cost based on the "points" used in creating your movie. You pay for your movie once you "publish" it. However, you don't have to pay while a movie is "in progress" so you could experiment to see if it is worthwhile to you. http://www.xtranormal.com/

4. Digital Story Telling: Explore this link for developing a digital storyboard: http://courseweb.lis.illinois.edu/~jevogel2/lis506/howto.html It includes both guidelines to digital story board creation and links to free software.

5. Blogging: www.blogger.com This works seamlessly with Google/Gmail.

6. Podcasting: http://audacity.sourceforge.net/ is a website for audio only podcasting. Easy to use. You can record sound, edit sound and save files in multiple formats.

7. Mind Mapping: There are several free mind mapping software programs available. The one used in the example came from Freemind. http://freemind.en.softonic.com/

8. Webpage: There are several software programs that you may choose to use for developing web pages such as Dreamweaver. You can also search the internet for webpage templates and find several free sites. Once such option is http://www.wix.com/create/website

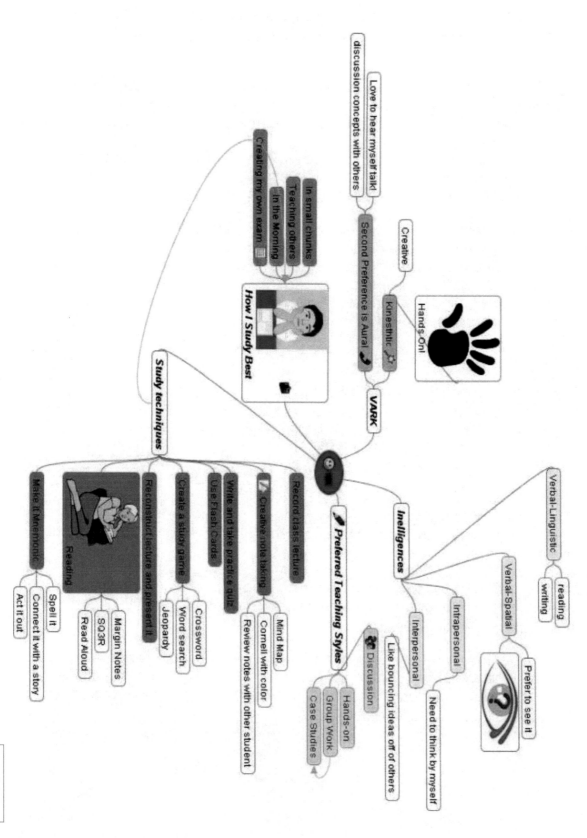

discussion concepts with others

Love to hear myself talk!

Second Preference is Aural

Creative

Kinesthetic

Hands-On!

VARK

How I Study Best

In small chunks

Teaching others

In the Morning

Creating my own exam!

Study techniques

Make it Mnemonic
- Act it out
- Connect it with a story
- Spell It

Reading
- Read Aloud
- SQ3R
- Margin Notes

Reconstruct lecture and present it

Create a study game
- Jeopardy
- Word search
- Crossword

Use Flash Cards

Write and take practice quiz

Creative note taking
- Review notes with other student
- Cornell with color
- Mind Map

Record class lecture

Preferred Teaching Styles
- Discussion
- Case Studies
- Group Work
- Hands-on

Intelligences
- Interpersonal
  - Like bouncing ideas off of others
- Intrapersonal
  - Need to think by myself
- Verbal-Spatial
  - Prefer to see it
- Verbal-Linguistic
  - writing
  - reading

Intentionally Left Blank

Core Assessment 4

Tutorial and Learning Services Learning Outcome:

Students will locate and utilize academic tutorial and learning resource services.

Academic Tutorial In-Class Assignment: Access the online tutorial services provided and complete the following tasks.
DUE: Class Session 9

1. **Study Stack (online –** www.studystack.com**) –** Here you can use pre-made flash cards from numerous subjects or create your very own flash cards, depending upon your desired content, allowing for very focused review. You can also take practice quizzes, study the flash cards, or even play games to learn the content.

   ☐ Access Study Stack by visiting www.studystack.com.
   ☐ Register as a new user by clicking "Free Sign Up" located on the upper right hand side of the screen.   You are only asked to provide a username, password, and e-mail address. (Suggestion, use your college email username and password.)
   ☐ Write your username here:
   _____.
   ☐ Write your password here:
   _____.
   ☐ Once you have created an account, click on "Home" in the upper left corner to return to the homepage.
   ☐ If you needed to access flash cards for Science, what five types of science are available?
      1. _____.
      2. _____.
      3. _____.
      4. _____.
      5. _____.
   ☐ Type "ACA 115" in the search bar.
      1. Select "ACA 115: Core 4 | Chapter 3: Learning Styles and Studying
      2. Study the flash cards by clicking them to flip and display the definition.
      3. How many terms are there? _____
      4. Scroll to the bottom of the page and view the numerous icons that can be used to study the terms. Try the "Matching" icon and play. Record how long it took you to complete. _____ (Timer is at the bottom of the matching list)
      5. Now try the "Quiz." How did you do? Record your score here: _____.
      6. Try "Hangman" or "Crossword". Did you get them correct? _____.
      7. FYI- You can create your own flash cards by clicking the "Create your own flashcards" link.

2. **SAS Curriculum Pathways and Writing Reviser** (online -
www.sascurriculumpathways.com) - SAS Curriculum Pathways and WritingReviser is a
free, self-help resource to assist students in five main subject areas: English, Math,
Science, Social Studies and Spanish. There are interactive tutorials and resources for
each subject. In addition, SAS Writing Reviser provides assistance with writing
assignments.

   Username: nccstudent   SAS Curriculum Pathways   WritingReviser
   No password is required

☐ From The Moodle Session block under assignments click on: " 🌐 SAS Curriculum
Pathway & Writer Reviser. " Log in as directed above.

☐ Under "Browse Resources" listed on the left hand side of the screen, record the 5 main
categories listed: English Language Arts, _____, Science,
_____ _____, _____.

☐ Under the Science category, select "Cells". From the list of resources, find the "Cell
Sizes" resource and read the description of the resource. (This video may not play due
to the plug-ins needed.) What question would you be able to answer after watching
the video based upon the description? _____
_____

3. **Smarthinking** (online – www.smarthinking.com) - Smarthinking is the online tutoring
service provided for Nash Community College students. Smarthinking can provide
assistance with math, writing, chemistry, physics, accounting, economics, anatomy and
physiology, biology, Spanish, nursing, and allied health.

   Username: nash0405
   Password: livetutors

☐ From The Moodle Session block under assignments click on:" 🌐 Smarthinking online
tutoring services."

☐ Use the above username and password to begin. You will be asked to set up your own
account with a username and password. Do so now. (Suggestion, use your college
email username and password in order to remember.)

☐ Once you are logged in you will be at the home page. Complete the list of buttons
found at the home page and fill in the blanks.
   1. <u>**Writing Center**</u> – Have your _____ reviewed by a tutor.
   2. _____ - Chat _____ with a _____ tutor.
   3. _____ _____ - Schedule to _____ with a _____ tutor in the
      _____.
   4. **Offline** _____ - Send a _____ an academic _____.

☐ Select the "Drop-In Tutoring" button.   Why are some subjects grayed out?
_____

☐ List one subject available for a live tutor right now: _____

☐ From the menu options at the top of the page, select, "Scheduled Tutoring."

☐ Scheduled sessions must be reserved _____ hours in advance.

☐ Name a subject listed that you might schedule a tutor for: _____

☐ From The Moodle Session block under assignments click on: 🌐 Sample session for
Smarthinking.

☐ Select and watch the nursing tutorial. (Note, flash is needed to view. Best watched from
a PC.) Bonus question…What two hormones does the Thyroid gland secrete?
_____ and _____.

o Visit the Nash Community College Library website: www.nashcc.edu/library

o There are 8 icons that represent a variety of databases and resources that are available to you as a student of Nash Community College.

Which icon would you select to...

1. Find a library book? _____

2. Obtain 24 hour assistance? _____

3. Read an electronic version of a book? _____

4. Explore international facts? _____

o Select the NC Live icon.

What is the username and password used to access library resources from home?

Username: _____

Password: _____

o From the NCLIVE homepage, go to the search box and input:

Note Taking Habits

   1. How many results did you get? _____

o Now try the search again, but this time **INCLUDE** quotation marks.

"Note Taking Habits"

   2. How many results did you get? _____

o Choose the following article:

Assisting students to avoid plagiarism

By clicking on the ▣ icon to the right of the blue title link, complete the following:

1. Author(s): _____
2. Source: _____
3. Volume & Issue: _____
4. Date the article was written: _____
5. Read the Abstract and answer the following question: This study looked at secondary school students from what country? _____

6. Now, click on the actual article. (The blue title of the article is the link) Find the "Cite" button and select it. 🖹 Cite

Find the MLA citation format for this article and record it here:

_____

_____

_____

Describe briefly the importance of citing sources:

_____

_____

When is it appropriate to cite sources?

_____

_____

o   Return to the NC Live homepage by clicking on the NC Live icon in the upper left corner of the screen.

NC LIVE

o   Here you will be able to choose links to numerous databases specific to many content areas.

Books & Literature	History & Biography
novels, poetry, criticism, plays, Worldcat	WWII, Civil War, presidents, world history
Business & Management	Hobbies & Interests
small business, company info, Morningstar, WSJ	books, auto repair, gardening

1. Dependent upon your current major or career goal, which database link would best supply you with information? _____

2. If you were told to write an essay on World War II, which database link would provide you with resources? _____

o   Select the Current Issues database link. Then, select the CQ Researcher Online link. **CQ Researcher is a great database for finding topics and articles on current events.**

1. What is today's Featured Report? _____

o   Click on the Pro/Con tab. (This can be used to obtain information on both sides of the topic.) List the two experts that are part of the pro/con debate.

2. Pro: _____

3. Con: _____

o   View the Hot Topics listed on the right side of the screen. Select a topic.

4. What topic did you select? _____

5. Each article begins with a topic question. What is your article's topic question?

_____

CORE ASSESSMENT 4 EVALUATION RUBRIC

ACA Tutorial & Learning Resource Services

Student accesses Study Stack.	5	
Student completes the Study Stack portion of the assignment accurately.	0 -15	
Student accesses SAS Curriculum Pathways and Writing Reviser.	5	
Student accesses Smarthinking.	5	
Student completes the Smarthinking portion of the assignment accurately.	0 -15	
Student answers Smarthinking bonus question accurately.	2	
Student accesses the library website and correctly completes the database and resource information on the form.	0-10	
Student accesses NC Live and completes a search for "Note Taking Habits."	0-10	
Student utilizes information from selected article and correctly completes the information on the form.	0-10	
Student includes MLA citation and satisfactorily explains the importance of citing sources.	0-10	
Student accesses CQ Researcher from NC Live and correctly completes the information as indicated on form.	0-15	
TOTAL POINTS	(0-100)	
LETTER GRADE	■	
RUBRIC SCORE	(0-4)	

GRADE RANGE	RUBRIC SCORE	DESCRIPTION
90-100	4	Exceeds Expectations
80-89	3	Meets Expectations
60-79	2	Partially Meets Expectations
1-59	1	Did Not Meet Expectations

0	0	Did Not Attempt Assignment

Intentionally Left Blank

Core Assessment 5   Due Date: _____

Note Taking Learning Outcome
Students will demonstrate effective note taking skills.

In-class assignment: Apply one of the note taking methods discussed in class during an in-class exercise and submit notes. Alternatively, if you are absent from class this day, take notes from the reading in the text book from pages 172 to 181 using either Cornell, Mindmap, Outlining or PowerPoint Miniatures (found on page 81-83 of this workbook) and submit.

Out-of-Class Assignment: Select and complete one of two note taking assignment options: Lecture Notes OR Reading Notes.

CHOOSE ONLY 1:
☐ **Option 1 LECTURE NOTES:** This assignment asks you to demonstrate note taking skills during a lecture. Choose any course other than ACA to complete this assignment and apply one of the lecture note taking techniques from Chapter 7 (pp. 184--190). Submit a copy of your notes along with the Note Taking Reflection form found on page 45-46 of this workbook. You must request permission to use the ACA course material if ACA is the only course you are taking or if your other coursework does not readily lend itself to lecture note taking.
  Choose any ONE of the following Note Taking techniques:
  - Cornell system
  - Mind mapping
  - PowerPoint miniatures
  - Parallel note taking
  - Outlining
  - 3 column math notes

  -OR-
☐ **Option 2 READING NOTES:** This assignment asks you to demonstrate note taking skills for a reading assignment. Using the "Read Right!" techniques described in Chapter 8 (pp. 207-212), choose any course other than ACA to complete this assignment. Submit a copy of your notes along with the Note Taking Reflection form found on páge 45-46 of this workbook. You must request permission to use the ACA course material if ACA is the only course you are taking.
  Choose any ONE of the following Read Right! Techniques:
  - Running commentary (Read Right! suggestion #4)
  - Margin Notes: what and why statements (Read Right! suggestion #5)
  - Write detailed notes using the Cornell, mind mapping, or Outlining system (Read Right! suggestion #6)
  - Use SQ3R (Read Right! suggestion #8) ** Use form on page 44 of the workbook.
  - Be Inventive (Read Right! suggestion #12)

Documentation of Completion for either option:

1. Turn in a copy of the lecture or reading notes to the instructor.
2. Complete the Note Taking reflection form and turn in with your notes.
** (Note, if you select SQ3R for option 2 Reading Notes, an additional completed reflection form is required found on page 44.)

SQ3R Documentation Form

Directions: Complete this only if you used the SQ3R method for option 2 READING NOTES. Answer in full sentences and in detail. The assignment will be graded based on the level of detail in your responses.

Name:

Course name and number:
Textbook title:
Title and page number of chapter(s) read:

Survey (What did you notice as you skimmed the text? Headers? Definitions? Exercises or activities?)

Question (Describe the what, why, and how questions that you asked yourself.)

     What is this chapter about?

     Why is it included?

     How might I use this information?

Read (Did you take notes while you read? What note taking method did you use? Attach a copy of the notes that you took while reading.)

Recite (Describe the reciting experience. Were you able to recite what you had read? Was it helpful to you?)

Review (Attach a copy of your written summary or type your summary below.)

Note Taking Reflection Form - Page 1 of 2

Directions: After completion of Note Taking Core Assessment 5, answer the following in full sentences and in detail. The assignment will be graded based on the level of detail in your responses. Attach a copy of your notes. If you use margin notes, you may photocopy a sample of pages from your text or re-write the notes, indicating the page and paragraph beside which you placed the notes.

Name:

1. Which note taking assignment option did you complete?

Option 1 LECTURE NOTES	Option 2 READING NOTES

If Option 1, which technique did you use?
 	
☐ Cornell system
☐ Mind mapping
☐ PowerPoint miniatures
☐ Parallel note taking
☐ Outlining
☐ Three-column math notes
	If Option 2, which technique did you use?
	
	☐ Running commentary
	☐ Margin notes
	☐ Write detailed notes:
	    ☐ Used Cornell system for detailed notes
	    ☐ Used Mind mapping for detailed notes
	    ☐ Used Outlining for detailed notes
	☐ SQ3R (<u>COMPLETE ADDITIONAL</u> SQ3R Reflection form)
	☐ Be inventive
	    Describe inventive strategy: _____

2. In which course did you take lecture or reading notes? What topic was being discussed?

Option 1 LECTURE NOTES	Option 2 READING NOTES
Course name and number: Instructor's name: Date of lecture: Time of class: Topic of discussion:	Course name and number: Title of the textbook: Chapter title: Page numbers:

Reflection continues to second page

<u>Note Taking Reflection Form</u> - Page 2 of 2

3. From your perspective, what are the positives of this method? If you did not find any positives, elaborate on why.

4. From your perspective, what negatives did you encounter? If you did not find any negatives, elaborate on why.

5. Will you use this lecture or reading note taking method again? Why or why not?

ACA Note Taking
CORE ASSESSMENT 5 EVALUATION RUBRIC

STUDENT NAME_____

☐ Option 1 LECTURE NOTES   or   ☐ Option 2 READING NOTES

Student completes in-class lecture note exercise or alternative textbook notes if absent from class.	5	
Student demonstrates ability to apply and understand selected note-taking technique by showing obvious consistency and diligence while completing the in-class lecture note exercise or alternative textbook notes.	0 - 25	
Student completes the Note Taking No Penalty Quiz.	10	
Student submits out of class Note-Taking Assignment.	5	
Students' Note-Taking Assignment is submitted with proper documentation and demonstrates ability to apply and understand selected note-taking technique by showing obvious consistency and diligence. (The SQ3R option has an additional form for proof of documentation.)	0 - 25	
Student submits completed note taking reflection form.	5	
Students' completed note taking reflection form and open-ended questions demonstrate an understanding of the note taking process and its impact.	0 - 25	
TOTAL POINTS	(0-100)	
LETTER GRADE		
RUBRIC SCORE	(0-4)	

CORE EVALUATION RUBRIC

GRADE RANGE	RUBRIC SCORE	DESCRIPTION
90-100	4	Exceeds Expectations
80-89	3	Meets Expectations
60-79	2	Partially Meets Expectations
1-59	1	Did Not Meet Expectations
0	0	Did Not Attempt Assignment

How to Make a Mind Map®

The 'Laws of Mind Mapping' were originally devised by Tony Buzan when he codified the use of imagery, color and association and coined the phrase 'Mind Mapping'. In the intervening 30 plus years, there have been many variations on the original 'Mind Map ' and the widespread usage of mapping software of various sorts, has dramatically changed what is possible.   The summary below is based on Buzan's structure (a 'Mind Mapping, how to' - details available in his many books) but we believe that whilst this structure is great for establishing well-structured maps that can be used in many different ways, variations on these rules or 'laws' are often sensible and appropriate - as long as they are based on an understanding of why the laws exist and what they are trying to help the mind mapper to achieve.

The Mind Map below was produced using iMindMap.

5. The structure that should develop will be a 'radiant hierarchy', with ideas radiating out from your central theme and main branches.

✓ Clear
Associations
Radiant
Hierarchical
Structure

1. Start at the centre of a blank, landscape page, ideally with a colourful image to represent your subject.

Blank
Landscape
Centre
Paper
Start

Fun
EMPHASIS
Style
Personal
Beauty

How to Mind Map

2. Use words and pictures throughout your map. Wherever possible use single KEY words, printed along a line. Each word or picture sits on its own line.

Use
Images
Colour
Words
Print
Single
Key

4. Experiment with different ways of linking and emphasising different aspects. Use highlighters, codes and arrows as necessary.

Thinner 2
Connect
Thicker
Lines
Word
Length
Image
Organic
Flowing

3. The lines make the associations between ideas as clear as possible. Make them flowing and organic, each line the same length as the word or image. Always ensure that lines connect to the end of the line at the previous level. Typically lines will be thicker at the centre and thinner further out.

1. Take a blank piece of paper, A4 or larger.	Blank paper allows 360° of freedom to express the full range of your cortical skills, whereas pre-drawn lines restrict the natural flow of your thoughts.
2. Use the paper in landscape orientation.	Words and images have more space in the direction we write, so they don't bump into margins as quickly.
3. Start in the center.	Thoughts start in the center of our mental world. The Mind Map page reflects this!
4. Make a central image that represents the topic about which you are writing/thinking: • Use at least three colors. • Keep the height and width of the central image to approx. 2" or 5 cm (proportionately larger for bigger paper). • Allow the image to create its own shape (do not use a frame).	A picture is worth a thousand words. It opens up associations, focuses the thoughts, is fun and results in better recall: • Colors stimulate the right cortical activity of imagination as well as capturing and holding attention. • This size gives plenty of space for the rest of your Mind Map, while making it large enough to be the clear focus of the topic. • The unique shape makes it more memorable and enjoyable. A frame makes the center a monotony of shape and disconnects the branches.
5. The main themes around the central image are like the chapter headings of a book: • Print this word in CAPITALS or draw an image. • Place on a line of the same length • The central lines are thick, curved and organic i.e. like your arm joining your body, or the branch of a tree to the trunk. • Connect directly to the central	The main themes, connected to the central image on the main branches, allow their relative importance to be seen. These are the Basic Ordering Ideas (BOIs) and aggregate and focus the rest of the Mind Map: • Printing (versus cursive) allows the brain to photograph the image thus giving easier reading and more immediate recall. • Word length equals line length. An extra line disconnects thoughts, length accentuates the connection. • Curved lines give visual rhythm and variety and so are easier to remember, more pleasant to draw and less boring to look at. Thicker central lines show relative importance. • Connected to the image because the brain works by association not separated, disconnected

image.	lines.
6. Start to add a second level of thought. These words or images are linked to the main branch that triggered them. Remember: • Connecting lines are thinner. • Words are still printed but may be lower case.	Your initial words and images stimulate associations. Attach whatever word or image is triggered. Allow the random movement of your thought; you do not have to 'finish' one branch before moving on: • Connected lines create relationships and a structure. They also demonstrate the level of importance, as from a branch to a twig. • The size and style of the letters provide additional data about the importance and meaning of the word/image.
7. Add a third or fourth level of data as thoughts come to you: • Use images as much as you can, instead of, or in addition to the words. • Allow your thoughts to come freely, meaning you 'jump about' the Mind Map as the links and associations occur to you.	Your brain is like a multi-handed thought-ball catcher. The Mind Map allows you to catch and keep whatever 'thought ball' is thrown by your brain.
8. Add a new dimension to your Mind Map. Boxes add depth around the word or image.	To make some important points stand out.
9. Sometimes enclose branches of a Mind Map with outlines in color: • Enclose the shape of the branch and hug the shape tightly. • Use different colors and styles.	The outlines will create unique shapes as you find in clouds and will aid your memory: • These provide immediate visual linking. They can also encourage follow-up and remind you of action you need to take. • They can also show connection between branches by using the same color outline.
10. Make each Mind Map a little more: • BEAUTIFUL • ARTISTIC • COLOURFUL • IMAGINATIVE and • DIMENSIONAL	Your eyes and brain will be attracted to your Mind Map: • It will be easier to remember. • It will be more attractive to you (And to others as well).
11. Have fun! Add a little humor, exaggeration or absurdity wherever you can.	Your brain will delight in getting the maximum use and enjoyment from this process and will therefore learn faster, recall more effectively and think more clearly.

The Cornell Note-taking System

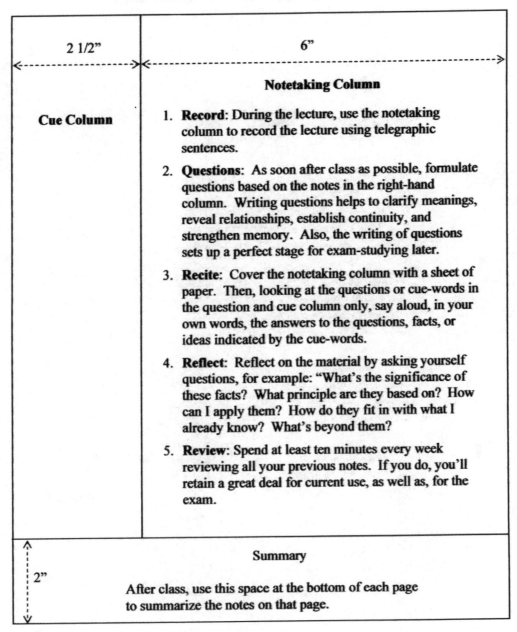

2 1/2"	6"
Cue Column	**Notetaking Column** 1. **Record**: During the lecture, use the notetaking column to record the lecture using telegraphic sentences. 2. **Questions**: As soon after class as possible, formulate questions based on the notes in the right-hand column. Writing questions helps to clarify meanings, reveal relationships, establish continuity, and strengthen memory. Also, the writing of questions sets up a perfect stage for exam-studying later. 3. **Recite**: Cover the notetaking column with a sheet of paper. Then, looking at the questions or cue-words in the question and cue column only, say aloud, in your own words, the answers to the questions, facts, or ideas indicated by the cue-words. 4. **Reflect**: Reflect on the material by asking yourself questions, for example: "What's the significance of these facts? What principle are they based on? How can I apply them? How do they fit in with what I already know? What's beyond them?" 5. **Review**: Spend at least ten minutes every week reviewing all your previous notes. If you do, you'll retain a great deal for current use, as well as, for the exam.

2"	Summary After class, use this space at the bottom of each page to summarize the notes on that page.

Adapted from How to Study in College 7/e by Walter Pauk, 2001 Houghton Mifflin Company

Structure of Three-Column Math Notes
from
ON COURSE: STRATEGIES FOR CREATING SUCCESS IN COLLEGE AND IN LIFE,
STUDY SKILLS PLUS EDITION by Skip Downing p. 168

Three Column Math Notes		
Problem	**Solution**	**Explanation**
Write down the math problem.	*Write the steps used to solve the problem.*	*Write in your own words how to do each step.*

Example Using Three Column Math Notes

Problem	Solution			Explanation

Problem: Find the first 5 *multiples* of 12 and 18

	12	18
1		
2		
3		
4		
5		

Set up a table to organize your work.

	12	18
1	**12**	
2	**24**	
3	**36**	
4	**48**	
5	**60**	

Multiply 12 by each number in column 1. Write the answer in column 2.

	12	**18**
1	12	**18**
2	24	**36**
3	36	**54**
4	48	**72**
5	60	**90**
	12	**108**

Multiply 12 by each number in column 1. Write the answer in column 3.

The Outlining Method

Dash or indented outlining is a traditional note taking method that can work for most subjects except for some science classes such as physics or math.
- The information which is most general begins at the left with each more specific group of facts indented with spaces to the right.
- The relationships between the different parts is carried out through indenting.
- No numbers, letters, or Roman numerals are needed.

Method
Listen and then write in points in an organized pattern based on space indention. Place major points farthest to the left. Indent each more specific point to the right. Levels of importance will be indicated by distance away from the major point. Indention can be as simple as or as complex as labeling the indentations with Roman numerals or decimals. Markings are not necessary as space relationships will indicate the major/minor points.

Advantages
Well-organized system if done right. Outlining records content as well as relationships. It also reduces editing and is easy to review by turning main points into questions.

Disadvantages
Requires more thought in class for accurate organization. This system may not show relationships by sequence when needed. It doesn't lend to diversity of a review attach for maximum learning and question application. This system cannot be used if the lecture is too fast.

When to Use
The outline format can be used if the lecture is presented in outline organization. This may be either deductive (regular outline) or inductive (reverse outline where minor points start building to a major point). Use this format when there is enough time in the lecture to think about and make organization decisions when they are needed. This format can be most effective when your note taking skills are super sharp and you can handle the outlining regardless of the note taking situation.

Example:

I) **Extrasensory perception**
   A) **-definition: means of perceiving without use of sense organs.**
   B) **-three kinds -**
      1) **-telepathy: sending messages**
      2) **-clairvoyance: forecasting the future**
      3) **-psychokinesis: perceiving events external to situation**
   C) **-current status -**
      1) **-no current research to support or refute**
      2) **-few psychologists say impossible**

Core Assessment 6   **Due Date:** _____

Test-Taking Learning Outcome:
Students will identify and describe test taking strategies.

In-Class Assignment: Identify and describe test taking strategies through classroom activities dealing with test anxieties, preparation for testing, and test integrity. Complete the following tasks:

1. Complete Exercise 9.3 Test Anxiety Survey on page 56 of this student workbook, to determine your level of anxiety. On page 57 of the student workbook, complete a 6-8 sentence reflection on the survey results.

2. Read the True/False section of Chapter 9 on pages 251 & 252 of the textbook. Pay close attention to the two tips that specifically discuss "absolutes" and "qualifiers." Use the worksheet on page 58 of this workbook to categorize key words into absolutes and qualifiers that can be clues to the correct answer in a true/false format. After completing the worksheet, add and categorize 3 additional words.

3. Form small groups in class and choose from one of the following activities to demonstrate your understanding of test-taking techniques and strategies.
   a. Develop at least 10 game show questions on test-taking strategies. The questions should contain a combination of true/false, multiple choice, and fill-in-the-blank questions. Consult pages 241-262. Your group will create a game show such as Jeopardy, Family Feud, or Are You Smarter than a Fifth Grader to play with the class. Each group will turn in its test-taking strategy questions and answer key.
   b. Collaborate with your group to develop what you consider to be the ten most important tips from the before, during, and after the test sections in your textbook. Consult pages 241-243, 249-251, and 260-262. Create a skit, song, or cheer based upon the top ten list and perform it for your classmates. Each group will turn in its top ten test-taking strategy tips.
   c. Create a visual display such as a Mind Map, poster, or graphic organizer that outlines 10 strategies and/or suggestions for taking multiple choice, true/false, essay, short answer, fill in the blank, and matching tests. Consult pages 251-258. Exhibit your visual display to your classmates and submit your creation to your instructor.

Out-of-Class Assignment: Identify one of your most challenging current courses. Using information on that course and your knowledge of your upcoming final exam, presentation, or essay; apply your preferred VARK learning style and complete the Master Study Plan on page 85 and 86 of the student workbook to create a detailed plan for your success.

Documentation of Completion:		
1. Surevy and reflection on test anxiety 2. Worksheet on key words 3. 10 item list from small group project 4. Master Study Plan		

Student completes Test Anxiety Survey	5	
Student completes reflection on Test Anxiety Survey results.	5	
Students' reflection is thoughtful and contains a minimum of 6-8 sentences.	0-10	
Student thoughtfully completes Key Word exercise and includes at least 3 additional key words.	0-10	
Student appropriately contributes and participates in a small group to complete a test-taking activity.	0 - 15	
Student submits documentation of completed test-taking activity, demonstrating thoughtful understanding and application of appropriate test-taking strategies. (Game Show questions, Top Ten List, or visual display.)	0 - 20	
Student submits completed Master Study Plan.	5	
Student thoughtfully completes Master Study Plan, demonstrating the ability to apply and understand techniques and strategies for success based upon their VARK learning style.	0 - 30	
TOTAL POINTS	(0-100)	
LETTER GRADE		
RUBRIC SCORE	(0-4)	

ACA Test-Taking Skills
CORE ASSESSMENT 6 EVALUATION RUBRIC

STUDENT NAME: _____

Group Members: _____

GRADE RANGE	RUBRIC SCORE	DESCRIPTION
90-100	4	Exceeds Expectations

80-89	3	Meets Expectations
60-79	2	Partially Meets Expectations
1-59	1	Did Not Meet Expectations
0	0	Did Not Attempt Assignment

Test Taking: High Anxiety?

Name: _____

Exercise 9.3 Test Anxiety Survey

What is test anxiety? What are the symptoms? Do you have it? Fill out the following informational survey to determine whether or not you may have test anxiety. For each of the twelve statement, rate your degree of agreement or disagreement.

1	2	3	4	5
Disagree	Disagree	Unsure	Agree	Agree
Completely	Somewhat		Somewhat	Completely

_____1.   I cringe when I suddenly realize on the day of an exam that I forgot about the test.

_____2.   I obsess about the possibility of failing an upcoming exam.

_____3.   I often experience disappointment, anger, embarrassment, or some other

emotional reaction during an exam.

_____4.   I think that instructors secretly get enjoyment from watching students squirm over exams.

_____5.   I experience physical symptoms such as an upset stomach, faintness, hyperventilation, or nausea

before an exam.

_____6.   I tend to zone out during exams; my mind goes blank.

_____7.   I feel extreme pressure to please others by doing well on exams.

_____8.   If I'm honest, I'd have to admit that I really don't' know how to study for tests.

_____9.   I'd much rather write a paper or give a presentation that take an exam.

_____10.   I usually fear that my exam grade will be lower than that of other students.

_____11.   After taking an exam, I obsess on my performance, going over and over questions that I think I

may have missed.

_____12.   I convince myself that I'm not good at taking exams even though I often do fairly well on them.

_____   **TOTAL (add up your score)**

If your score equals 49-60, you are a likely candidate for test anxiety.

If you scored between 37-48, you have some signs of anxiety and may need help in managing your stress level.

If you scored 36 or below, you most likely experience a normal amount of anxiety and have already developed coping skills to help you.

TEST-TAKING HIGH ANXIETY REFLECTION

Take a moment to think about what your results from the Test-Taking Anxiety Survey mean for you as a student. Complete a 6-8 sentence reflection paragraph discussing your results, areas of concern and steps you could take to help reduce your test-taking anxiety or outline those behaviors you practice to help you cope with test taking anxiety.

NAME: _____ TEST ANXIETY SCORE: _____

_____

_____

_____

_____

_____

_____

_____

_____

_____

_____

_____

_____

_____

_____

_____

_____

True/False Exercise

Name: _____

Read the True/False section of Chapter 9 on pages 251 & 252 of the textbook. Pay close attention to the two tips that specifically discuss "absolutes" and "qualifiers." Categorize the key words into absolutes and qualifiers that can be clues to the correct answer in a true/false test question. Absolutes tend to make the answer false and qualifiers tend to make the answer true. After completing the worksheet, add and categorize 3 additional words.

Key Word	Absolutes	Qualifiers
Always		
Sometimes		
Only		
A few		
Commonly		
Never		
Biggest		
More		
Might		
May		
100%		
Least		
Frequently		
Typically		
Without a doubt		
Nobody		
Better		
Entirely		
Smartest		
Smarter than		
No one		
Largest		
Larger than		
Average		
All		
Most		
Worst		
Everyone		
Occasionally		
Everybody		

NOW, ADD YOUR OWN WORDS

Your ACA Instructor <u>may</u> offer additional options for this assignment. Please verify directions/options with him or her before completing the Final Project.

In class final project: (25 points)

<u>Dream Big Collage:</u> Following your instructors directions, you will complete your collage during a class session.

Out of class final project: (75 points)
<u>Select one of the following options:</u>

⌘ OPTION 1 : TEACHING SUCCESS
Directions: Write a letter to someone you love (your child, grandchild, brother, sister, etc.). Tell the person how he/she can create a successful life. Share <u>three or more specific strategies</u> you have learned in our class.

Please write the letter thoughtfully and thoroughly. It should be at least 1 page, double spaced, 12 point font and a minimum of 500 words.

If the person you write to is very young (or not even born yet), you may want to give the letter as a gift when he/she is old enough to benefit from your wisdom.

Here is the beginning of a sample....

> Dear Ronald,
>
> I'm writing this letter in hopes that I may share with you some of the most valuable information that I've received in my entire life. This semester I took a course entitled ACA 115.........
>
> The strategies that I learned while taking this course have helped me to grow significantly in all areas of my life, and I want you.......
>
> My personal definition of success is....
>
> The first strategy that I recommend to you is .....

⌘ OPTION 2: LETTER TO NEXT SEMESTER'S STUDENTS
Directions: Write a letter to NEXT SEMESTER'S students. What would you say to new students coming to college about this course? What did you learn that you consider important? (Be sure to include 3 or more strategies) Why was this class important to you? What advice would you give that student to achieve success?

Please write the letter thoughtfully and thoroughly. It should be at least 1 page, double spaced, 12 point font and a minimum of 500 words.

A sample of the Option 2 letter is located on the back of this page.

Here is the beginning of a sample....

Dear Future ACA 115 Students,

I'm writing this letter in hopes that I may share with you some of the most valuable information that you will need to know about ACA 115.....

The most important pieces of information that I learned while in the class was.....

The first strategy that I learned about and recommend to you is .....

Looking back, this class was very important even though I didn't think so at first. However, I.....

If I could give you any advice about achieving success it would be.....

****

♮ OPTION 3: LIVING YOUR SUCCESS

Project into the future that you have successfully graduated from college (NCC plus whatever other professional training is needed to get a job in your career area). See the career counselor to get specific information. Also, use the information on your career that we gathered in the computer lab.
You are now very successful in your career, and the principal from your high school or a favorite teacher has invited you back to the high school to speak to seniors about your present employment and life, why you chose the particular career that you did, your career successes, any situations that were difficult to overcome, what you feel has made you a success, and any words of encouragement that you have to offer these prospective graduates.

Creativity: Suits are not expected unless you want to go that far, but dress the part to the best of your ability. For example, if you are a nurse, you may be able to borrow some nursing wardrobe or equipment that would add to your presentation. Be creative. Let's be serious, but also have fun with this. You will be speaking to a very respectful audience who will be impressed with your accomplishments.

PowerPoint: You need to create a PowerPoint presentation to accompany your presentation. A minimum of 5 slides is required. The presentation should be between 5-10 minutes.

Criteria:
____1. The presenter speaks in a volume that the audience can hear.
____2. The speaker maintains as much eye contact as possible. Note cards may be used, but we hope that you will talk to us as much as possible and avoid reading to us from cards. Another student may assist by moving the slides forward at the speaker's indication.
____3. Practice is apparent.
____4. Knowledge of the career is apparent.
____5. A minimum of five slides.

SESSION HANDOUTS
AND INFORMATION

Find an Expert

Find someone in our group with expertise in each of the areas described. As you circulate around the room, introduce yourself, fill in your interviewee's first name below, describing your own experience as it relates and something in particular your interviewee knows about the subject that you don't. Find someone...

1. Who knows a lot about **cars**?
   Name: _____

2. Who has had a piece of **writing published**?
   Name: _____

3. Who is a **fast food** junkie?
   Name: _____

4. Who knows how **families** work as a result of having five or more siblings?
   Name: _____

5. Who knows the campus because a **friend or sibling previously attended**?
   Name: _____

6. Who's had a stellar career in **high school athletics**?
   Name: _____

7. Who's never gotten anything but **A's in math**?
   Name: _____

8. Who studied **art or dance** growing up?
   Name: _____

9. Who knows the food service industry well from working as a **server**?
   Name: _____

10. Who is a relationship expert as a result of a **long-lasting romance**?
   Name: _____

Finally, what kind of expertise do you hope to develop during your first term in college?

_____

Social Contract

In groups, discuss the behaviors you would like to see all class members exhibit that promote learning and foster a meaningful class experience. What behaviors should students avoid? Record those items you would like to see included in a class social contract that we will all agree to abide by. Here is a sample, however, focus on your desires for the most optimum class environment!

Sample In-Class Social Contract

- We are comfortable exploring tangents, but we will not get upset when the teacher reins us back in to move on. Anyone in the class is allowed to remind us to get back on task.
- Everyone is responsible to the rest of us for having done the reading.
- Only attack ideas, not people in the class.
- We can all make a mistake with the language we use, but some words are just too surprising and you should avoid them. Four-letter words and anything racist will upset a lot of us.
- Using your laptop is okay, but not for computer games, social networking sites, stuff unrelated to class. If you're on those, sit further back in the room so we aren't seeing it from behind you.
- No cell phones should be on during class. Annoying rings and texting notices are too much.
- Only ask for a paper extension if you really are deathly ill. Otherwise the rest of us are likely to resent it.

Record your group's suggestions for a class social contract. When complete, Access the " Social Contract Shared Google Document" in your Moodle Session 1 block to submit your suggestions. As a class you will collaborate to finalize the document.

Envision Excellence

Excellence in academics is often measured in terms of grades, with an "A" grade representing the highest achievement. Consider what it takes to be a successful student. First individually, then in small groups, do the following activities.

1. INDIVIDUALLY: Answer these 2 questions.
   - What makes someone an "A" student?

   - What qualities does "A" work possess?

2. INDIVIDUALLY: Read the article from NISOD Innovation Abstracts *Calatrello's Highly Unscientific Theory of Halves: A Primer for Student Success*. As you read the article, circle key terms and underline important details.

3. IN GROUPS: Write a 20/20 reflection from the article. As a group summarize the article in 20 words.

Record your 20 word summary here:

4. IN GROUPS: Compare your answers to the first question, what qualities makes an A student. Then answer the following question:
    -   What are the behaviors of successful students? Record at least 7. Be prepared to share answers to the whole class.

5. INDIVIDUALLY: After the whole class discussion, consider the behaviors listed on the board and select at least 3 successful student behaviors you will commit to this semester and complete the following sentence:

    This semester I _____ *will commit to* _____

    _____

    _____

    _____

    _____.

Choices of Successful Students

SUCCESSFUL STUDENTS...	STRUGGLING STUDENTS...
1. ... accept **PERSONAL RESPONSIBILITY** seeing themselves as the primary cause of their outcomes and experiences.	1. ... seeing themselves as Victims, believing that what happens to them is determined primarily by external forces such as fate, luck, and powerful others.
2. ... discover **SELF-MOTIVATION**, creating positive energy in their lives by discovering personally valuable goals and dreams.	2. ... having difficulty sustaining motivation, often feeling depressed, frustrated, and/or resentful about a lack of purpose in their lives.
3. ... master **SELF-MANAGEMENT**, consistently planning and taking purposeful actions in pursuit of their goals and dreams.	3. ... seldom identify specific actions needed to accomplish a desired outcome. And when they do, they tend to procrastinate.
4. ... employ **INTERDEPENDENCE,** building mutually supportive relationships that help them achieve their goals and dreams (while helping others do the same).	4. ... are solitary, seldom requesting, even rejecting, offers of assistance from those who could help.
5. ... gain **SELF-AWARENESS**, consciously employing behaviors, beliefs, and attitudes that keep them on course.	5. ... make important choices unconsciously, being directed by self-sabotaging habits and outdated life scripts.
6. ... adopt **LIFE-LONG LEARNING**, finding valuable lessons and wisdom in nearly every experience they have.	6. ...resist learning new ideas and skills, viewing learning as fearful or boring rather than as mental play.
7. ... develop **EMOTIONAL INTELLIGENCE,** effectively managing their emotions in support of their goals and dreams.	7. ... live at the mercy of strong emotions such as anger, depression, anxiety, overwhelm or a need for instant gratification.
8. ... **BELIEVE IN THEMSELVES**, seeing themselves as capable, loveable and unconditionally worthy human beings.	8. ... doubt their competence and personal value, feeling inadequate to create their desired outcomes and experiences.

From Skip Downing: *On Course: Strategies for Creating Success in college and in life.* Houghton Mifflin

24 Hour Time Management Boxes

6am	7am	8am	9am	10am	11am
5am	**To Do:**				12noon
4am					1pm
3am					2pm
2am	**Notes:**				3pm
1am					4pm
12midnight					5pm
11pm	10pm	9pm	8pm	7pm	6pm

6am	7am	8am	9am	10am	11am

To Do:

5am					12noon
4am					1pm
3am					2pm

Notes:

2am					3pm
1am					4pm
12midnight					5pm

11pm	10pm	9pm	8pm	7pm	6pm

Calendar Activity

Assignment: Add you school related events and the NCC shared calendar to your Google Calendar.

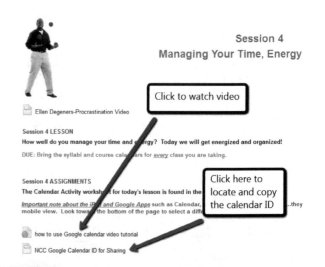

1. Watch the video tutorial on Moodle found in Session 5 block under assignments: How to use Google calendar video tutorial. (Your instructor may opt to show to entire class.)
2. From Moodle access the NCC Google Calender ID found in the Session 5 block under asissignments.

3. Copy the ID. For iPad users, touch and hold the screen for a few a seconds to pull up the copy option. You will

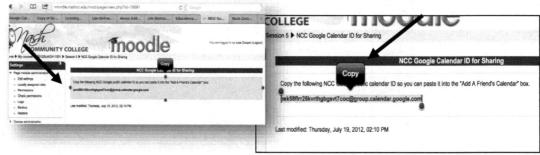

have to adjust the size of the area so you only capture the ID in blue. Then tap the copy button.

4. Now leave Moodle and log in to your student gmail account and access the Google calendar.

Make sure YOU are logged in
(and not a previous student!)

5. For iPad users, you want your calendar to display in "desktop" view NOT "mobile."

On the iPad, to switch from mobile view to desktop view, click desktop view at the bottom of the screen and select cancel when you get the warning.

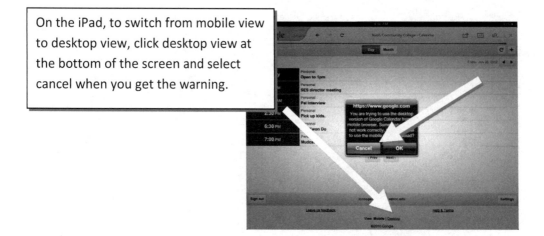

6. With your Google calendar open, paste the NCC Calendar ID in the box under "Other Calendars." <u>For iPad users,</u> touch the box until the paste option appears, then tap paste. And press enter (or Go on the iPad.)

7. You have added the NCC Calendar! Be sure it is selected so all the NCC events appear.

8. Now it's time to add your academic events! Consult your syllabi and activity calendars from all the other courses in which you are enrolled.

9. **ADD EVENTS!** Add *all* due dates such as tests, papers or projects for each class. You can even add smaller personal due dates that help prepare for tests or papers such as complete study guide, revise notes, start research, select topic, etc. Don't forget all the Core Assessments and assignments for ACA!

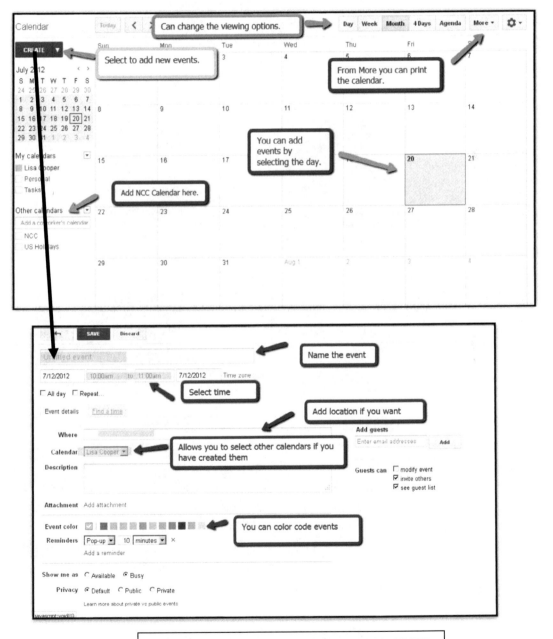

YOU CAN PRINT YOUR CALENDAR WHEN COMPLETE

Responsibility Model

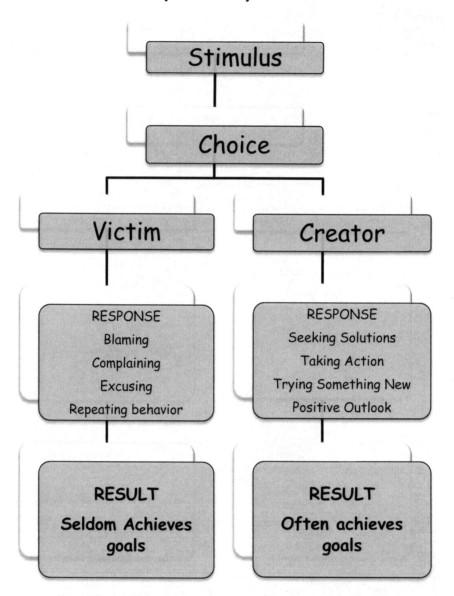

The key ingredient of personal responsibility is choice. Numerous times each day, you come to a fork in the road and must make a choice. Even not making a choice is a choice. Some choices have a small impact: Shall I get my hair cut today or tomorrow? Some have a huge impact: Shall I stay in college or drop out? The sum of the choices you make from this day forward will create the eventual outcome of your life. **The Responsibility Model** shows what the moment of choice looks like. In that brief moment between stimulus and response, we can choose to be a Victim or a Creator. At critical forks in the road, Victims waste their energy and remain stuck, while Creators use their energy for improving their outcomes and experiences.

The Language of Responsibility

Victim Language	Creator Language
Victims believe that their outcomes and experiences are determined by forces beyond their control, such as powerful others and luck. They believe they are merely pawns in the chess game of life. Their language is characterized by **blaming, complaining, and excusing.**	Creators believe that their outcomes and experiences are the natural consequences of their choices. They believe they are chess masters who **create, promote,** or **allow** all that happens in their lives. Their language is characterized by **ownership** and **action** plans.
1. I'm terrible in this subject.	I find this course challenging, so I'll start a study group and ask more questions in class.
2. The instructor is so boring he puts me to sleep.	I'm having difficulty staying awake in this class, so I'm going to ask permission to record lectures. Then I'll listen to them a little at a time and take detailed notes.
3. This course is a stupid requirement.	I'm going to ask my instructor to help me see how this course will benefit me in the future.
4. I couldn't get the assignment because I was absent.	
5. I can't help talking or texting in class.	
6. I couldn't come to class because I had to go to the dentist for a checkup.	
7. I work nights so didn't have time to do my homework.	
8. My friend got me so angry, I can't even study for the exam.	
9. I'll try to do my best this semester.	
10. I hate group projects because people are lazy and I always end up doing most of the work.	
11. If they'd do something about the parking on campus, I wouldn't be late so often.	
12. I am failing my online class because the site is impossible to navigate.	
13. I'm too shy to ask questions in class even when I'm confused.	
14. I wish I could do better in math, but I just can't.	

Case Study in Critical Thinking:
Strange Choices

"Do your students make really strange choices?" Professor Assante asked.

The other professors looked up from their lunches. "What do you mean?" one asked.

At the beginning of each class, I give short quizzes that count as 50 percent of the final grade," **Professor Assante** replied. "One of my students comes late to every class, even though I keep telling her that there is no way she can pass the course if she keeps missing the quizzes. But, she still keeps coming late! What is she thinking?"

"That's nothing," **Professor Buckley** said "I've got a really bright student who attends every class and offers great comments during discussions. But the semester is almost over, and he still hasn't turned in any assignments. At this point, he's too far behind to pass. Now that's what I call a strange choice."

"You think that's strange, **Professor Chen** said, "I'm teaching composition in the computer lab. Last week I sat down next to a woman who was working on her essay, and I suggested a way she could improve her introduction. I couldn't believe what she did. She swore at me, stormed out of the room, and slammed the door."

Professor Donnelly chimed in. "Well, I can top all of you. In my philosophy class, participation counts for one-third of the final grade. I've got a student this semester who hasn't said a word in twelve weeks. Even when I call on him, he just shakes his head and says something under his breath that I can't hear. One day after class, I asked him if he realized that if he didn't participate in class discussions, the best grade he could earn is a D. He just mumbled, "I know.' Now there is a choice I don't get!"

"How about this!" **Professor Egret** said. "I had a student last semester with a B average going into the final two weeks. Then he disappeared. This semester, I ran into him on campus, and asked what happened. 'Oh' he said, 'I got burned out and stopped going to my classes.' 'But you only had two more weeks to go. You threw away thirteen weeks of work,' I said. You know what he did? He shrugged his shoulders and walked away. I wanted to shake him and say, 'What is wrong with you?'"

Professor Fanning said, "Talk about strange choices. Last week I had four business owners visit my marketing class to talk about how they promote their businesses. Near the end of the period, a student asked if the business owners had ever had problems with procrastination. While the panelists were deciding who was going to answer, I joked, 'Maybe they'd rather answer later.' Okay, it was weak humor, but most of the students chuckled, and then one panelist answered the question. The next day I got a call from the dean. The student who'd asked the question about procrastination told him I'd mocked her in front of the whole class, and now she's going to drop out of college. I had videotaped the class, so I asked her if she'd be willing to watch the tape. Later she admitted I hadn't said what she thought I had, but she still dropped out of school. What is it with students today and their bizarre choices?"

Listed below are all the professor's students. Choose the one you think made the strangest choice and speculate why this student made the choice. Dive deeper than the obvious answers such as "He's probably just shy." Why do you suppose he is shy? What past experiences might the inner conservation of this Inner Critic and Inner Defender sound like? What emotions might he often feel? What beliefs might he have about himself, other people, or the world? In what other circumstances (e.g. work, relationship, and health) might a similar choice sabotage his success?

_____ Professor Assante's Student
_____ Professor Buckley's Student
_____ Professor Chen's Student
_____ Professor Donnelly's Student
_____ Professor Egret's Student
_____ Professor Fanning's Student

> Diving Deeper: Recall a course you once took in which you made a choice that your instructor might describe as "strange." Explain why you made that choice. Dive deep, exploring what really caused your choice.

Case Study in Critical Thinking: The Late Paper

Professor Freud announced in her syllabus for Psychology 101 that final term papers had to be in her by noon on December 18. No student, she emphasized would pass the course without a completed term paper turned in on time. As the semester drew to a close, **Kim**, had an "A" average in Professor Freud's psychology class, and she began researching her term paper with excitement.

Arnold, Kim's husband, felt threatened that he had only a high school diploma while his wife was getting close to her college degree. Arnold worked the evening shift at a bakery, and his coworker **Philip** began teasing that Kim would soon dump Arnold for a college guy. That's when Arnold started accusing Kim of having an affair and demanding she drop out of college. She told Arnold he was being ridiculous. In fact, she said, a young man in her history class had asked her out, but she had refused. Instead of feeling better, Arnold became even angrier. With Philip continuing to provoke him, Arnold became sure Kim was having an affair, and he began telling her every day that she was stupid and would never get a degree.

Despite the tension at home, Kim finished her psychology term paper the day before it was due. Since Arnold had hidden the car keys, she decided to take the bus to the college and turn in her psychology paper a day early. While she was waiting for the bus, **Cindy**, one of Kim's psychology classmates, drove up and invited Kim to join her and some other students for an end-of-semester celebration. Kim told Cindy she was on her way to turn in her term paper, and Cindy promised she'd make sure Kim got it on time. "I deserve some fun," Kim decided, and hopped into the car. The celebration went long into the night. Kim kept asking Cindy to take her home, but Cindy always replied, "Don't be such a bore. Have another drink." When Cindy finally took Kim home, it was 4:30 in the morning. She signed with relief when she found that Arnold had already fallen asleep.

When Kim woke up, it was 11:30 A.M., just thirty minutes before her term paper was due. She could make it to the college in time by car, so she shook Arnold and begged him to drive her. He just snapped, "Oh sure, you stay out all night with your college friends. Then, I'm supposed to get up on my day off and drive you all over town. Forget it." "At least give me the keys," she said, but Arnold merely rolled over and went back to sleep. Panicked, Kim called Professor Freud's office and told **Mary**, the secretary, that was having car trouble. "Don't worry," Mary assured Kim, "I'm sure Professor Freud won't care if your paper's a little late. Just be sure to have it here before she leaves at 1:00." Relieved, Kim decided not to wake Arnold again; instead, she took the bus.

At 12:15, Kim walked into Professor Freud's office with her term paper. Professor Freud said, "Sorry, Kim, you're fifteen minutes late." She refused to accept Kim's term paper and gave Kim an "F" for the course.

Listed before are the characters in this story. Rank them in order of their responsibility for Kim's failing grade in Psychology 101. Give a different score to each character. Be prepared to explain your choices.

Most responsible ← 1 2 3 4 5 6

_____ **Professor Freud**, the teacher
_____ **Kim**, the psychology student
_____ **Arnold**, Kim's husband
_____ **Philip**, Arnold's coworker
_____ **Cindy**, Kim's classmate
_____ **Mary**, Professor Freud's secretary

DIVING DEEPER: Is there someone not mentioned in the story who may have also bear responsibility for Kim's failing grade?

The "Who Stays?" Problem

The Dilemma

Enrollment has been cut back at this college. As a member of the board, it is your responsibility to rank the following ten students according to who deserves to remain in this college, number 1 being the most deserving. Each of these students has been enrolled for about seven weeks. Descriptions of their pre-college situations and performances, as well as the circumstances of their college career, thus far, are listed.

Factors to Keep in Mind

Each student's potential, abilities, or capabilities
Each student's motivation to preform
The degree of difficulty in conquering problems
The availability of services to help overcome those problems
The outcome of his or her education: how badly each wants to achieve
The probability of successful completion of a college education

The Students

Angela: Extremely intelligent; senior class valedictorian; has won awards in the National Science Fair for exhibits; received a full scholarship from a national company to the college of her choice; has much difficulty relating to others on a social basis; has definite plans to major in chemistry; an out-of-state student; is having great difficulty adjusting to dorm life; is homesick.

Albert: An All-State quarterback in high school plans to play college football on a full scholarship; scored extremely poorly on the college admittance tests although his high school were average; has no major; plans to become a coach; poor classroom attendance.

Jill: Ranked in the middle of her graduating class; did fair in high school math; did poorly in high school science; parents pushed her toward her declared major in biology; doing poorly in these college subjects; has good study habits; high capabilities in English; lives at home; family problems are developing

Carolyn: A divorced mother with two children; 24 years old; has returned to college to continue her college education after dropping out six years earlier; is working and raising her family; commutes; major is a two year degree in secretarial sciences; receives financial aid

Dominique: An exchange student from Venezuela; lives in a men's dorm; visiting our college for one semester; has already earned a degree in his own country; doing very well academically; involved in several campus organizations; self-supported; here to experience our lifestyle; not working toward any major.

Thomas: Outgoing and well-liked among his peers; poor grades; studied little in high school and has few study skills; undecided on major; his parents pay for his education; an in-state student, lives on campus; enjoys the college party life most of all.

Howard: Ranked in the top 5 percent of his graduating class; out-of-state student; lives on campus; came from an influential family in a small town; was "Mr. Popular" in high school; is having a terrible time adjusting to college life; very homesick; grades are dropping as time passes; uninvolved in campus life; has much potential that could be used.

Gina: An accounting major; dropped all but 9 hours of classes; very poor classroom attendance; extremely active in her sorority; poor grades; parents pay for everything; in town student; lives on campus; her parents donate a scholarship each year.

Evelyn: 63 years old; worked in a daycare center for the past 15 years; prior to that was a housewife and mother; is working toward a degree in child psychology; receiving financial aid for returning students over 60; doing well academically.

Karl: Average grades; commutes; works 20 hours a week to pay for his education; is aiming for a degree in engineering; would like to get involved in more activities on campus but does not have the time; high potential in math; hard worker.

Only the top 5 students will be allowed to remain in school.
Who will stay? Who will go?

1.

2.

3.

4.

5.

6.

7.

8.

9.

10.

Note Taking Checklist

Listening, Engaging and Note-taking

Step 3: What are my choices?

- ☐ Assemble appropriate supplies- paper, pencil, etc.
- ☐ Do the assigned reading
- ☐ Complete homework assignments before attending class
- ☐ Go over notes from previous class sessions
- ☐ Prepare a list of questions
- ☐ Eliminate distractions- don't sit with your best friend, turn off cell phone, etc.
- ☐ Attend every class – show up physically!
- ☐ Posture counts- sit up in class
- ☐ Arrive early and choose a good seat
- ☐ Don't talk while others are speaking
- ☐ Be organized (ID your notes)
- ☐ Listen actively for key concepts, main ideas supporting material
- ☐ Write down examples or key words from stories that will help anchor the main points
- ☐ Note whether a handout accompanies lecture materials
- ☐ Listen and look for gestures and statements that communicate, "This is important" or "Be sure to include this in your notes."
- ☐ Ask and answer questions- Speak up!
- ☐ When in doubt, write it down
- ☐ Watch for visual cues
- ☐ Stay focused! (Take a deep breath, keep the worries and to-do lists at bay)
- ☐ Take notes with this system: _____
- ☐ Speed up note-taking—consult shorthand list on page 183
- ☐ Record the class if needed
- ☐ Polish notes within 24 hours
- ☐ Manipulate your notes (For example, fill in charts, draw diagrams, retype notes, create a mind map, underline, highlight, organize, copy notes to flash cards, cut up a copy of your notes and put it back together again – work with your notes!
- ☐ Paraphrase – put your notes in your own words
- ☐ Summarize your notes

☐ Compare notes

Intentionally Left Blank

Cornell Note Paper

FOCUS	Name:
	Class:
	Date:
Topic/Objective:	Essential Question:

Questions/Main Ideas:	Notes:

Summary:

FOCUS

Name:

Class:

Date:

Topic/Objective:

Essential Question:

Questions/Main Ideas:	Notes:

Summary:

PowerPoint Miniatures

Using Lecture Notes

Manipulating involves working with your notes by typing them out later.

Paraphrasing is the process of putting your notes into your own words.

Summarizing is a process of writing a brief overview of all of your notes from one lecture.

Exercise 7.4:
Note-Taking 414

© 2012 Wadsworth, Cengage Learning

_____

_____

_____

_____

_____

_____

_____

Get Engaged in Class

What actually correlates with success are not grades, but 'engagement'—genuine involvement in courses and campus activities. Engagement leads to 'deep learning,' or learning for understanding. That's very different from just memorizing stuff for an exam, then forgetting it.
John Merrow, reporter, USA Today

© 2012 Wadsworth, Cengage Learning

_____

_____

_____

_____

_____

_____

_____

Dare to Prepare

1. Look ahead.
2. Do the assigned reading.
3. Show up physically.
4. Show up mentally.
5. Choose your seat strategically.
6. Bring your tools.
7. Don't sit by your best friend.
8. Posture counts!
9. Maintain your health.
10. Focus.

© 2012 Wadsworth, Cengage Learning

_____

_____

_____

_____

_____

_____

_____

The Rules of Engagement

1. **Be aware that gab is not a gift.**
   In class, talking while others are speaking is inappropriate.

2. **Control Your Hunger.**
   Get in the habit of eating before or after class and not during.

3. **Turn off your cell phone, please!**
   Yes, we can hear your phone vibrating, too. And texting in class shows where your attention *really* is.

4. **Better late than never?**
   Arriving late and leaving early disturbs students and instructors.

5. **Actively choose to engage, not disengage.**
   You must make a conscious decision to become engaged.

© 2012 Wadsworth, Cengage Learning

Soft vs. Hard Listening

SOFT Listening Skills:
-- Used in emotionally charged situations.
-- You must be accepting, sensitive, and nonjudgmental.
-- You don't have to assess, analyze, or conclude.

HARD Listening Skills:
-- Used in classroom/educational situations.
-- Pay close attention and think critically.
-- Evaluate, analyze, and make decisions about new information.

© 2012 Wadsworth, Cengage Learning

Listening with Focus

➢ Calm yourself.
➢ Be open.
➢ Don't make snap judgments.
➢ Assume responsibility.
➢ Watch for gestures that say "Here comes something important!"

➢ Listen for speech patterns that subtly communicate "Make sure you include this in your notes!"
➢ Uncover general themes or roadmaps for each lecture.
➢ Appreciate your instructor's prep time.

"You cannot truly listen to anyone and do anything else at the same time.
M. Scott Peck, American author

Exercise 7.14
Listening

© 2012 Wadsworth, Cengage Learning

Adapt to a Variety of Lecture Styles

The Rapid-Fire Lecturer   The Slow-Go Lecturer   The All-Over-the-Map Lecturer   The Content-Intensive Lecturer

The Review-the-Text Lecturer   The Go-Beyond-the-Text Lecturer   The Active-Learning Lecturer

Exercise 7.2: Multitasking

© 2012 Wadsworth, Cengage Learning

Ask and You Shall Receive

Have you ever decided NOT to ask a question in class because you thought:

- I don't want to look stupid.
- I must be slow. Everyone else seems to be understanding.
- I'm too shy.
- I'll get the answer later from the text.
- I don't think my question is important.
- I don't want to interrupt the lecture; the instructor's on a roll.
- I'm sure the instructor knows what he's talking about. He must be right.

The next time you find yourself in a situation where you don't understand something, consider these points:

1. Remember that you're not in this alone.
2. Ask academically relevant questions when the time is right.
3. Save personally relevant questions for later.
4. Build on others' questions.

© 2012 Wadsworth, Cengage Learning

QUIZ TIME!

© 2012 Wadsworth, Cengage Learning

Intentionally Left Blank

Master Study Plan

What is my learning style: _____

This means I should:

_____

_____

EXAM I AM PREPARING FOR:	
DAY & DATE of EXAM:	
WHAT WILL THE TEST COVER? • How long will it be? • Is there a study guide? • What content is covered? • What materials, text, should I use? • What types of questions will be on it? Objective: multiple choice, T/F, matching; Subjective: fill-in-the-blanks, short answer or essay	

Best location for me to study:	
Best time for me to study:	
Do I need to study alone, or with others?	
Anything else I should do to make sure my study time is effective?	
Challenges or distractions I may encounter:	Possible solutions to overcome these challenges:
Study Strategies I use	Study Strategies I will try:

CONTENT I NEED TO LEARN	BEST STRATEGY TO USE (Consult your VARK list, Memory Devices or search online)

HOW DO I KNOW WHEN I AM DONE STUDYING CHECKLIST?

☑	Item to-do	Goal Date:
	Find out when, where & how long the test will be	
	Find out what it will cover, request a study guide	
	Schedule my study times	
	List the content I need to learn and select the study strategies I will use	
	Gather all the supplies and reading materials I will need	

STUDY SCHEDULE

I should start studying on: _____

INCLUDE ON YOUR CALENDAR **When** you will study and **What** you will accomplish (i.e. make note cards, create quiz, read & take notes, review notes, re-organize notes, make a chart or drawing, create and practice a mnemonic and device, etc.) Use the template provided or put on your own personal calendar.

Monday	Tuesday	Wednesday	Thursday	Friday	Saturday	Sunday

Components of Emotional Intelligence

One of psychology's open secrets is the relative inability of grades, IQ, or SAT scores, despite their popular mystique, to predict unerringly who will succeed in life... At best, IQ contributes about 20 percent to the factors that determine life success, which leaves 80 percent to other forces... IQ offers little to explain the different destinies of people with roughly equal promises, schooling, and opportunity.   *Daniel Goleman*

1. **EMOTIONAL SELF-AWARENESS: Knowing your feelings in the moment.** Self-awareness of one's own feelings as they occur is the foundation of emotional intelligence and is fundamental to effective decision making. Thus, people who are keenly aware of their changing moods are better pilots of their lives. For example, emotional self-awareness helps you deal effectively with feelings of overwhelm instead of attempting to escape them by watching television.

2. **EMOTIONAL SELF-MANAGEMENT: Managing strong feelings**. Emotional Self-Management enables people to make wise choices despite the pull of powerful emotions. People who excel at this skill avoid making critical decisions during times of high drama: instead they wait until their inner storm has calmed and then make considered choices that contribute to their desired outcomes and experiences. For example, emotional self-management helps you resist dropping an important class simply because you got angry at the teacher. It also helps you make a choice (e.g., writing a term paper) that offers delayed benefits instead of a choice (e.g. attending a party) that promises instant gratification.

3. **SOCIAL AWARENESS: Empathizing accurately with other people's emotions.** Empathy is the fundamental "people skill." Those with empathy and compassion are more attuned to the subtle social signals that reveal what others need or want. For example, social awareness helps you notice and offer comfort when someone is consumed by anxiety or sadness.

4. **RELATIONSHIP MANAGEMENT: Handling emotions in relationships with skill and harmony.** The art of relationships depends, in large part, upon the skill of managing emotions in others. People who excel at skills such as listening, resolving conflicts, cooperating and articulating the pulse of a group do well at anything that relies on interacting smoothly with others. For example, relationship management helps a person resist saying something that might publicly embarrass someone else.

After Math

When **Professor Bishop** returned mid-term exams, he said, "In 20 years of teaching math, I've never seen such low scores. Can anyone tell me what the problem is?" He ran a hand through his graying hair and waited. No one spoke. "Don't you people even care how you do?" Students fiddled with their test papers. They looked out of the window. No one spoke.

Finally, Professor Bishop said, "Okay, Scott, we'll start with you. What's going on? You got a 35 on the test. Did you even *study*?" **Scott**, 18, mumbled, "Yeah, I studied. But I just don't understand math." Other students in the class nodded their heads. One student muttered, "Amen, brother."

Professor Bishop looked around the classroom. "How about you Elena? You didn't even show up for the test." **Elena**, 31, sighed. "I'm sorry, but I have a lot of other things besides this class to worry about. My job keeps changing my schedule, I broke a tooth last week, my roommate won't pay me the money she owes me, my car broke down, and I haven't been able to find my math book for three weeks. I think my boyfriend hid it. If one more thing goes wrong in my life, I'm going to scream!"

Professor Bishop shook his head slowly back and forth. "Well, that's quite a story. What about the rest of you?" Silence reigned for a full minute. Suddenly **Michael**, 23, stood up and snarled, "You're a damn joke, man. You can't teach, and you want to blame the problem on us. Well, I've had it. I'm dropping this stupid course. Then I'm filing a grievance. You better start looking for a new job!" He stormed out of the room, slamming the door behind him.

"Okay, I can see this isn't going anywhere productive," Professor Bishop said. "I want you all to go home and think about why you're doing so poorly. And don't come back until you're prepared to answer that question honestly." He picked up his books and left the room. Elena checked her watch and then dashed out of the room. She still had time to catch her favorite show in the student lounge.

An hour later, Michael was sitting alone in the cafeteria when his classmates Scott and **Kia**, 20, joined him. Scott said, "Geez, Michael, you really went off on Bishop! You're not really going to drop his class are you?" "Already did!" Michael snapped as his classmates sat down. "I went right from class to the registrar's office. I'm outta there!"

I might as well drop the class myself, Kia thought. Ever since she was denied entrance to the nursing program, she'd been too depressed to do her homework. Familiar tears blurred her vision.

Scott said, "I don't know what it is about math. I study for hours, but when I get to the test, I get so freaked it's like I never studied at all. My mind just goes blank." Thinking about math, Scott started craving something to eat.

"Where do you file a grievance against a professor around here, anyway?" Michael asked. "I have no idea," Scott said. "What?" Kia answered.

Michael stood and stomped off to file a grievance. Scott when to buy some French fries. Kia put her head down on the table and tried to swallow the burning sensation in her throat.

Listed below are the characters in this story. Rank them in order of their emotional intelligence. Give a different score to each character. Be prepared to explain your choices.

Most emotionally intelligent < 1 2 3 4 5 > Least emotionally intelligent

__Professor Bishop   __Scott   __Elena   __Michael   __Kia

Diving Deeper: Imagine that you have been asked to mentor the person whom you ranked number 5 (least emotionally intelligent). Other than recommending a counselor, how would you suggest that this person handle his or her upset in a more emotionally intelligent manner?

From Downing, On Course: Strategies for Success in College and in Life, Houghton Mifflin

ASSESSING EMOTIONAL INTELLIGENCE

Your Character:_____   Average of Four Scores:_____

Low Emotional Intelligence <- 1 2 3 4 5 6 7 8 9 10 -> High Emotional Intelligence

Emotional Self-Awareness: Knowing your feelings in the moment.
Character's specific behavior(s) that influenced your score.

Emotional Self-Management: Managing strong feelings.
Character's specific behavior(s) that influenced your score.

Social Awareness: Empathizing accurately with other people's emotions.
Character's specific behavior(s) that influenced your score.

Relationship Management: Handling emotions in relationships with skill and
harmony. Character's specific behavior(s) that influenced your score.

SWOT Analysis

Strengths	Opportunities
Weaknesses	Threats

How can you minimize weaknesses and threats and capitalize on strengths and opportunities?

RESOURCE INFORMATION

NCC Tutorial Service Options

1. **Math Tank** (S&T building 7106)-Individual tutorial assistance is available for math homework. Computerized programs are available for developmental math. Math re-testing is also conducted here.

2. **PAL (Peer Assisted Learning) Tutor Connection Program**
   PAL Tutor Connection Program is an appointment based peer tutoring initiative that connects students who need extra support with Peer Tutors who have demonstrated proficiency in select courses. Students interested in tutoring can fill out a <u>PAL Tutor Connection Request Form</u> found on the Nash website under the "Students" tab/Academics/Campus Tutoring. For more information about the PAL Tutor Connection Program contact: Student & Enrollment Services, 252-451-8219

3. **Smarthinking** (online – <u>www.smarthinking.com</u>) - Smarthinking is the online tutoring service provided for Nash Community College students. A handout with additional details for accessing this resource is located in CampusCruiser. Smarthinking can provide assistance with math, writing, chemistry, physics, accounting, economics, anatomy and physiology, biology, Spanish, nursing, and allied health.
   Username: nash0405
   Password: livetutors
   ** **After logging the first time with the above information, you will be asked to set up an account and create your own log in and password.**

4. **SAS Curriculum Pathways and Writing Reviser** (online - <u>www.sascurriculumpathways.com</u>) - SAS Curriculum Pathways and WritingReviser is a free, self-help resource to assist students in five main subject areas: English, Math, Science, Social Studies and Spanish. There are interactive tutorials and resources for each subject. In addition, SAS Writing Reviser provides assistance with writing assignments.
   Username: nccstudent
   No password is required

Student Organizations

Nash Community College realizes the role of student organizations in enhancing a student's college experience. These organizations provide the students and the college with regional, state, and national exposure via participation in their respective chapter affiliations and campus social activities.

Artistic Designers Club

The Artistic Designers Club is an organization for students who are enrolled in cosmetology courses at Nash Community College. The club encourages and provides opportunities for development of leadership skills and accountability in the cosmetology field.
Advisor: Karey Parker
Phone: 451-8377
Email: kparker@nashcc.edu

Criminal Justice Club

The Criminal Justice Club gives students the opportunity to gain exposure to the professional realm of law enforcement, courts, and corrections.
Advisor: Carmi Guyette
Phone: 451-8375
Email: cguyette@nashcc.edu

Culinary Club

The Culinary Club is designed to encourage students in the Culinary or Hotel and Restaurant Management (HRM) programs to polish and perfect skills learned in the Culinary and HRM curriculum.

Advisor: Co Advisor:
Don Sexauer   Carlos Quagliaroli
Phone: 451-8362   Phone: 451-8366
Email: Email:
dsexauer@nashcc.edu cquagliaroli@nashcc.edu

Drama Club

The Drama Club encourages support and participation in activities of theater interest. This includes participation in campus productions at Nash Community College as well as supporting and participating in activities which enhance theatrical development.
Advisor: Lisa Cooper
Phone: 451-8223
Email: lcooper@nashcc.edu

Early Childhood Education Club

The Early Childhood Education Club is an organization for students who are pursuing a degree or certificate in Early Childhood. Students are encouraged to become actively involved in local, state and national professional activities in Early Childhood Development.
Advisor: Sarah Prezioso
Phone: 451-8317
Email: sprezioso@nashcc.edu

Gamma Beta Phi Society

GBP is the honor society on campus. Students must have a 3.0 or higher cumulative grade point average, must have earned 12 or more semester hours in a major at NCC. Membership drives are held in September and February of each semester.
Advisor: Natasha Neal
Phone: 451-8256
Email: nneal@nashcc.edu

M.A.L.E.

Men Achieving Leadership and Excellence (M.A.L.E.) promotes academic, personal & professional success for minority males at Nash CC.
Advisor: Keith Smith
Phone: 451-8264
Email: ksmith@nashcc.edu

Math & Science Club

The Math & Science Club provides opportunities to develop leadership, critical thinking and advocacy skills in mathematics and science.
Advisor: Kochi Angar   Co Advisor: Dave Beamer
Phone: 451-8396   Phone: 451-8334
Email: kangar@nashcc.edu Email: dbeamer@nashcc.edu

Metal Workers Club

The Metal Workers Club is an organization to promote skills, technology and knowledge for students in the Machining, Welding, and Industrial Systems Technology programs.
Advisor: George Shook   Co Advisor: Jay Manning
Phone: 451-8283   Phone: 451-8270
Email: gshook@nashcc.edu Email: jamanning@nashcc.edu

Nash Community Lambda Association of Students and Supporters (NCLASS)

NCLASS is an organization with a goal to provide outreach, support, information, and resources for gay, lesbian, transgender, and bisexual students, faculty and staff, and for their families or friends. The club also provides information and resources for the College on issues regarding sexuality and sexual orientation while promoting a culture of fairness and equality for all NCC students and a social outlet for members and their friends.
Advisor: Sarah Prezioso
Phone: 451- 8317
Email: sprezioso@nashcc.edu

Phi Beta Lambda

PBL is an organization open to all curriculum students who are interested in the business field. PBL is the college-level counterpart of FBLA.
Advisor: Nakisha Floyd
Phone: 451-8299
Email: nfloyd@nashcc.edu

Phi Theta Kappa

Phi Theta Kappa is an international honor society that recognizes and encourages scholarship among 2-year college students. Students must have completed a minimum of twelve (12) semester hours of non-developmental course work and have earned a cumulative grade point average of 3.50 or higher.
Advisor: Robin Latham
Phone: 451-8213
Email: rlatham@nashcc.edu

Published Ink

Published Ink is a club which is open to any curriculum student at NCC who has an interest in writing, visual arts, marketing or publication. Its main purpose is to foster the production of creative writing and visual arts among the students of the College. By offering seminars and workshops, the club seeks to help students refine their skills. The club strives to produce a juried literary and visual arts magazine once a year.
Advisor: Robin Latham Co- Advisor: Debbie Lee
Phone: 451-8213   Phone: 451-8388
Email: Email:
rlatham@nashcc.edu dlee@nashcc.edu

Rock Solid Fellowship

Rock Solid Fellowship is a Christian organization open to all curriculum students who desire to worship Christ at Nash Community College through Bible studies, outreach, and various activities.
Advisor: Lori Sherick
Phone: 451-8483
Email: lsherick@nashcc.edu

Student Government Association (SGA)

The Student Government Association (SGA) is the primary organization responsible for providing activities and opportunities such as blood drives, fall/spring festivals, campus events and student talent shows. Through a democratic system of government, SGA enhances the formal educational experience and protects the rights and privileges of all students. Every curriculum student at NCC is a member of SGA and may attend all meetings.
Advisor: Kara Deans
Phone: 451-8218
Email: kdeans@nashcc.edu

Student Ambassadors

The Nash Community College Foundation sponsors a Student Ambassador program for selected individuals who demonstrate leadership, scholarship, and strong written and oral communication skills. Ambassadors represent Nash Community College at foundation events and a wide variety of school functions. Ambassadors assist the college during times such as registration and open house. Ambassador applications are available in the spring. In the spring of each year, a selection committee appointed by the Nash Community College Foundation Executive Director interviews and selects the ambassadors. Ambassadors receive a scholarship and serve the college in the subsequent school year.
Interim Advisor: Cheryl Gordon
Phone: 451-8230
Email: cgordon@nashcc.edu

Student Nurses' Association

The Student Nurses' Association is a pre-professional organization for student nurses at NCC. Membership is open to nursing and pre-nursing students.
Advisor: Cheryle Traish
Phone: 451-8211
Email: ctraish@nashcc.edu

Steps to Apply for Financial Aid

1. Apply for a Pin Number

   If you do not have a pin number to apply for federal aid, apply on the following website: www.pin.ed.gov . You may request a pin number at that time or have them to email one to you. You must have an active email address for your pin number to be sent to you. If you are a dependent student, a parent must apply for a pin number also. Please place your pin number in a safe place, because this will be your pin number as long as you received financial aid.

2. Fill out the FAFSA (Free Application for Federal Student Aid) for the current year
   a. Complete the application at www.fafsa.ed.gov
   b. Select "Start Here"
   c. For accurate tax information utilize the feature for the IRS Data Retrieval Tool. Nash Community College strongly recommends all students, parents, and spouses (if applicable) to use the IRS Data Retrieval Tool. In order to do so, all parties must have already filed the previous year taxes at least three weeks prior to filling out the FAFSA.
   d. **NCC's school code---008557**
   e. If you filled out your FAFSA without a pin number, print out the signature page and mail it to the address on the same page. Your application will be processed faster if you use your pin number.
   f. Submit your FAFSA. The website produces a confirmation page that you have successfully transmitted your FAFSA. You may note the confirmation number and your estimated Expected Family Contribution (EFC).
   g. This confirmation is not an award letter. You must be approved by the institution you will be attending.
   h. Check your campus e-mail (given by NCC's admissions office) for further documentation that may be required by NCC's Financial Aid Department.
   i. Submit all required documentation.
   j. Await an Award notification by e-mail and mail (check your WebAdvisor account for updates as well).

Intentionally Left Blank

JOURNAL 1

ACA–Journal

Name _____

Note to Students: *The purpose of the journal is to encourage you to reflect on the material covered in class and to apply the discovered concepts to your class work and life. The journal will be most meaningful if you complete it during or immediately after a class session. A quality reflection should be at least a ½ page of reflective thought.*

1 | Journal Entry– Class Session 1
Chapter 1 of Text

What life lesson did you gain or observe in the "Welcome to College Game?"

_____

_____

_____

_____

_____

_____

_____

_____

_____

_____

_____

_____

_____

_____

_____

_____

_____

2 | Journal Entry
Chapter 4 of Text

Write about the system (or lack of a system) that you presently use to decide what to do each day. What keeps you on track? What distracts you? Write about how you could use or adapt any of the concepts discussed in class to improve your time management and daily organization.

_____

_____

_____

_____

_____

_____

_____

_____

_____

_____

_____

_____

_____

_____

_____

_____

3 Journal Entry
Chapter 3 of Text

Identify something you have learned simply because you enjoyed learning it. What did you do to learn the information or skill? How often did you engage in learning this? How did you feel when you engaged in learning this? What were the rewards?

_____

_____

_____

_____

_____

_____

_____

_____

_____

_____

_____

_____

_____

_____

_____

_____

4 | **Journal Entry**
Chapter 2 of Text

MY PERSONAL RULES FOR SUCCESS IN COLLEGE AND IN LIFE:
Write a list of your own rules for achieving success. Which of your rules is most important and why? Which rules are easiest for you to follow and why? Which rules will challenge you the most to keep? Why?

_____

_____

_____

_____

_____

_____

_____

_____

_____

_____

_____

_____

_____

_____

_____

_____

_____

5 Journal Entry
Chapter 7 of Text

Describe the note taking challenges you are having (or can foresee having) in your courses. How would you like your situation to be? Based on class discussion, what two steps can you take to create your ideal note-taking situation?

_____

_____

_____

_____

_____

_____

_____

_____

_____

_____

_____

_____

_____

_____

_____

_____

_____

_____

6 Journal Entry
Chapters 8 and 9 of Text

Reflect on the question, "How do you know when you are done"? For example, how do you know when you are done studying for a test? Writing a paper? Reading? Make a checklist for yourself (the more specific and detailed, the better). How will that list help you in your studies?

_____

_____

_____

_____

_____

_____

_____

_____

_____

_____

_____

_____

_____

_____

_____

_____

7 Journal Entry
Chapter 9 of Text

List the courses you are taking this semester. Review the list of memory tips from the text. For each class, write about one or two tips that might help you remember material for that specific class.

8 | Journal Entry
Chapter 9 of Text

What challenges are you having (or can foresee having) with taking tests in the courses you are now taking? How would you like your present situation to be? Create your own "test smart" plan. What are some tips you will try?

9 | Journal Entry
Chapter 10 of Text

Based on the reading, how strong do you feel your emotional intelligence is? What areas would you want to improve? What is the first step you can take in doing that?

_____

_____

_____

_____

_____

_____

_____

_____

_____

_____

_____

_____

_____

_____

_____

_____

_____

_____

_____

10 Journal Entry
Chapters 11 and 12 of Text

What is the life lesson you discovered during the graduate game?

_____

_____

_____

_____

_____

_____

_____

_____

_____

_____

_____

_____

_____

_____

_____

_____

_____

_____

August 2015

Sun	Mon	Tue	Wed	Thu	Fri	Sat
26	27	28	29 Last day of Summer Cla	30 Faculty/Staff Workdays	31	Aug 1
2	3 Faculty/Staff Workdays	4	5	6 Last Day to Pay for fall WebAdvisor closes for f:	7	8
9	10 Faculty/Staff Workday	11 Faculty/Staff Profession:	12 Extended Registration for Fall 2015 WebAdvisor opens for e	13	14 WebAdvisor closes for e	15
16	17 First Day of Classes	18	19	20	21	22
23	24	25	26	27	28	29
30	31	Sep 1	2	3	4	5

September 2015

Sun	Mon	Tue	Wed	Thu	Fri	Sat
30	31	Sep 1	2	3	4	5
6	7 College Closed-Labor [	8	9	10	11	12
13	14	15	16	17	18	19
20	21	22	23	24	25	26
27	28	29	30	Oct 1	2	3

October 2015

Sun	Mon	Tue	Wed	Thu	Fri	Sat
27	28	29	30	Oct 1	2	3
4	5	6	7	8	9	10
11	12 Fall Break-No Classes	13	14	15	16	17
18	19	20	21	22	23	24
25	26	27	28	29	30	31

November 2015

Sun	Mon	Tue	Wed	Thu	Fri	Sat
Nov 1	2	3	4	5	6	7
8	9	10	11 College Closed-Veterar	12	13	14
15	16	17	18	19 Registration for Spring 2016	20	21
22	23	24 No Classes-Faculty Workdays	25	26 College Closed-Thanksgiving Holiday	27	28
29	30 Last day to Withdraw fro	Dec 1	2	3	4	5

December 2015

Sun	Mon	Tue	Wed	Thu	Fri	Sat
29	30 Last day to Withdraw fro	Dec 1	2	3	4	5
6	7	8	9	10	11	12
13	14	15	16 Last day of classes	17 Faculty/Staff Workdays	18	19
20	21 College Closed-Christmas Holidays	22	23	24	25	26
27	28 College Closed-Faculty/Staff Conservation Days	29	30	31	Jan 1 College Closed-New Ye	2

January 2016

Sun	Mon	Tue	Wed	Thu	Fri	Sat
27	28	29	30	31	Jan 1	2
	College Closed-Faculty/Staff Conservation Days				College Closed-New Ye	
3	4	5	6	7	8	9
	Faculty/Staff Workday	Extended Registration for Spring 2016				
10	11	12	13	14	15	16
	First Day of Classes					
17	18	19	20	21	22	23
	College Closed-MLK H(					
24	25	26	27	28	29	30

February 2016

Sun	Mon	Tue	Wed	Thu	Fri	Sat
31	Feb 1	2	3	4	5	6
7	8	9	10	11	12	13
14	15	16	17	18	19	20
21	22	23	24	25	26	27
28	29	Mar 1	2	3	4	5

March 2016

Sun	Mon	Tue	Wed	Thu	Fri	Sat
28	29	Mar 1	2	3	4	5
6	7	8	9	10	11	12
13	14	15	16	17	18	19
20	21	22	23	24	25 College Closed-Good F	26
27	28 Easter Break-No Curriculum Classes	29	30	31	Apr 1	2

April 2016

Sun	Mon	Tue	Wed	Thu	Fri	Sat
27	28	29	30	31	Apr 1	2
	Easter Break-No Curriculum Classes					
3	4	5	6	7	8	9
10	11	12	13	14	15	16
			Registration for Summer 2016 & Fall 2016			
17	18	19	20	21	22	23
					Last day to Withdraw or	
24	25	26	27	28	29	30

May 2016

Sun	Mon	Tue	Wed	Thu	Fri	Sat
May 1	2	3	4	5	6	7
8	9	10 Last day of Classes-Foll	11 Faculty/Staff Workdays	12 Graduation-GED/Adult H Nurses' Pinning	13 Graduation-Curriculum	14
15	16 Faculty/Staff Workdays	17	18	19	20	21
22	23 Extended Registration or Summer 2016	24	25 First Day of Classes-SU	26	27	28
29	30 College Closed-Memori	31	Jun 1	2	3	4

June 2016

Sun	Mon	Tue	Wed	Thu	Fri	Sat
29	30 College Closed-Memori	31	Jun 1	2	3	4
5	6	7	8	9	10	11
12	13	14	15	16	17	18
19	20	21	22	23	24	25
26	27	28	29	30	Jul 1	2

July 2016

Sun	Mon	Tue	Wed	Thu	Fri	Sat
26	27	28	29	30	Jul 1	2
3	4 College Closed-July 4th	5 College Closed-Faculty/Staff Conservation Days	6	7	8	9
10	11	12	13 Registration for Fall 2016	14	15	16
17	18	19 Last day to withdraw	20	21	22	23
24	25	26	27 Last day of Classes Su..	28	29	30
31	Aug 1	2	3	4	5	6

Mk.	Room # Series	Description	Contains
A	2000, 2200	Building A	Student & Enrollment Services, Library, Classrooms, Offices, Information Technology
B	2100	Building B	Classrooms, Offices, Learning Center
B&I	1000	Business & Industry Center	Bookstore, Cashier, Administrative Offices, Continuing Education, Brown Auditorium, Culinary
C	3000	Building C	Classrooms, Offices, Shops
CO		Commons	Midway Cafe
D1, D2	4000	Building D	Classrooms, Offices, Nursing, Humanities
E	5000	Building E	Maintenance, Classrooms, Offices
CDC	6000	Child Development Center	Child Care, Offices, Early Childhood Education
EC		Early College	High School
F		Electric Line Construction Technology Training Field	Electric Line Construction Training
POPAT		Police Officer's Physical Agility Training	Burn Laboratory
S&T	7000	Science & Technology Center	Classrooms, Offices, Radio, Biology, Chemistry

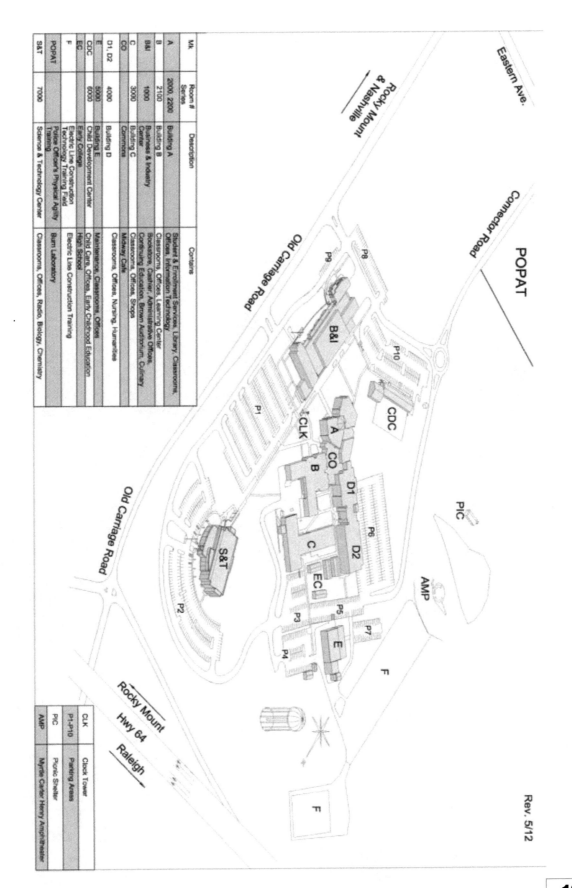

Eastern Ave.

Rocky Mount & Nashville

Connector Road

POPAT

Old Carriage Road

Rocky Mount

Hwy 64

Raleigh

CLK	Clock Tower
P1–P10	Parking Areas
PIC	Picnic Shelter
AMP	Myrtle Carter Henry Amphitheater

127